Best regards from

Lucy and Bill Carver

August 1966

VILLAGE DOWN EAST

VILLAGE DOWN EAST

Sketches of Village Life · on the northeast
coast of New England · before "gas-buggies"
came · by John Wallace · from conversations
with Zackary Adams · Duck Trap Cove · Maine

THE BOND WHEELWRIGHT COMPANY · FREEPORT · MAINE

"Gid-ap!"

Library of Congress Catalog Card Number: 66-23588

Printed in the United States of America

Summit, New Jersey 07901

THIS EDITION PUBLISHED BY THE BOND WHEELWRIGHT CO., FREEPORT, MAINE 04032.

PREFACE TO SECOND EDITION

JOHN WALLACE was, in fact, Will R. Davis, artist, humor-ist, and all 'round "sweetheart" of a man. He was never famous because he didn't want fame nor lots of money. He was, however, an artist in the true sense of the word. His techniques in many media, oils, crayon, water-color, pastel (he even made his own colors) were without flaw. His pen and ink work and his charcoal drawings in this volume speak for themselves, as do his writing and his sense of humor.

Born and raised in Lincolnville, Maine (which really has a "Duck Trap"), Will Davis remained a New Englander all his life. He lived in Boston and in his later years married, at last, a girl he had known in art school. They settled down in Rock-port, Massachusetts, but had less than three years together before he died.

Although Mr. Davis chose to do this book anonymously and to change the names of its characters, the people and events herein were very real and quite true to the era and area about which he writes.

Those of us who knew and loved Will Davis have caused his book to be re-published as a lasting memorial to as fine a man as God could create.

W.S.C.

The old seaman

INTRODUCTION

THE artist has pictured the old seaman sitting in the sun on a timber from an ancient wreck, surveying his altered world. But the artist was fortunate enough, too, to have known him as he had been, before the coming of the gasoline motor, which, as time went on, began to link his small, Maine coast communities together like beads strung on an asphalt chain, and, one by one, eliminated the white triangles of sails from the horizon line.

It had been a time and a way of life like the man it produced: detached, independent, unhurried; a time when corn huskings, quilting parties, berry pickings, barn raisings, made a pleasant social occasion of a part of manual labor; a time when cordwood and kerosene heated and lighted the home, and the only light on the road at night was the lantern one carried.

Isolated was the life in these communities, and the necessity of their isolation bred in the individual an imperturbable self-sufficiency. He would turn his hand with enthusiasm to almost any "job of work" that came along, whether it was the digging of a new ditch, laying up a stone wall, building a new rocking chair for his "woman," or precisely fitting together the structure of a boat.

It is as he was that the artist presents him here—with moments of grimness to be sure — but more typically with the penetrating humor and keen observation bred from nearness to the soil and the sea — as he was and his world was — a world of the past — uncluttered and somehow clean.

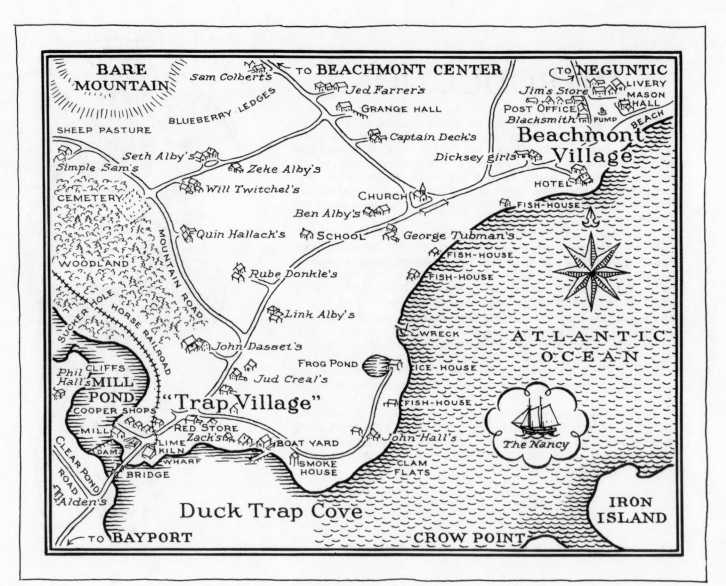

"The Shore"

CONTENTS

The Boston Boat

THE BOSTON BOAT

AS you say, it is a nice overnight trip down here on the steamer; specially if you crawl out early as she's comin' up the bay in the mornin' and there's a fair sunrise over the islands.

The fust time I went to visit my brother Mat in Vermont I took the boat as fur as Bostin — only time I'd ever trav'lled aboard a steam vessel. 'Twuz the ole "Augusty." The wind wuz easterly durin' the night with a tolable sea runnin', and what b'tween the way the ole craft twisted and creaked, and a paddle-wheel sloshin' 'longside my bunk, I didn't sleep none to speak of.

Enjoyed it more comin' home in July, tho the boat wuz considable crowded. A lot-a folks had to sleep in their clo'es on mattresses the darkies put round on the mail saloon floor. Good thing 'twuz a calm night, for even so, some wuz pale and spleeny.

Made myself known to the cap'n, explainin' that I wuz the fisherman who'd hailed him many a mornin' off Pollock Ledge. He said he'd whis'le next time he see me, and I'm proud to say he did.

The mail stage has alw'ys met the steamer at Bayport, mornin's, for any pass'ngers, baggage, or freight to be dropped along the twenty-six mile of road to Neguntic, the next boat stop no'th.

Jeff Dunkle wuz shippin' some apples to Bostin by boat last October, and thot he'd go along, visit the big market, and sight-see the city. He never wuz more'n twenty-thutty miles from home in his life and no hand to go on the water. 'Cordin' to him, 'twuz a rough night and he 'lowed he felt a mite "gaggy" till he chawed a piece of strip-fish he'd took along to settle his stomick.

The size of Bostin impressed Jeff considable. He swore he stood on a corner — by Summer and Washin'ton Street — much's half an hour, watchin' folks go by, and "never see a soul" he knew.

9

Jeff Dunkle

"Emma switched into the house"

THE MAIL STAGE

THE stage had quite a list to port yist'd'y when she come through, and no wonder; three-hunderd pounds or more of live-cargo wuz aboard'f'er, on the shady side: our hefty and comfort-lovin' Town Constable, Freeman Jackson Jubb.

It stopped at Emmy Smith's to leave her berry pails and some medicine. What a fidgety, fast-talkin' little ole maid she is! She refused Free once, and lived to regret it — "in sack-cloth and ashes," as her ma said. When she see him, she throwed up her hands:

"Well, of all things, Freeman Jubb, if it hain't you; big as life and twice as natural! — awful glad to see you, Freeman — how be you these days, Freeman? — hee hee — goodness me, Freeman!"

"Poorly, Emmy," says he, in his modrit way, "poorly, but jest as full of play as I alw'ys wuz. 'Member the time the hammock broke when I grabbed ye for a kiss? Still cute, Emmy! — it must be that Solomon's Sasperilli you take (they do say it's most thutty percent)."

"Oh, hush yer noise, Freeman Jubb! and do let bygones be bygones, and don't cast no spersions at my medicine, neither!" Then she settled accounts with Cal, for sellin' her blueb'ries. and gittin' the bottle of medicine and switched into the house.

Dunno what we'd do without Cal Frisbie and the stage. He not only carries the mail, freight, pass'ngers, and baggage (and gossip), but will do errants and tradin' for you. Never writes nothin' down, nor fails to keep all his orders and accounts straight, in his head. Evry minute he's drivin' he chatters and chaws, with a toothpick stuck in his mouth (tho he only has one tooth), and his red, paint-brush beard — if you've noticed — nigh brushin' the tip of his nose.

Talks to himself or the hosses if there don't happ'n to be no pass'ngers, twitchin' the reins and cluckin' evry few seconds — "G'long! Freddie an' Frankie!" (What names for hosses!)

11

Cal Frisbie

"We made Kesters Harbor"

FOG

FOG'S so durn thick this mornin' you kin hardly spit — but it's alw'ys been a part of the climate here, and after all, the fish bite just as well, or better, if you got instinc' enough to locate 'em.

Summer folks do the most complainin' 'bout fog, but friend Phil, the artist, takes it, as he says, "philsophical." He gen'ly has some picture putterin' to do indoors, and studies and reads considable. Don't read much, m'self, but do do a powerful lot-a thinkin' (considerin' the heft of bone there is b'tween my ears).

But fog ain't no friend to sailer men and accounts for many a wreck along the coast. Wuz in a bad wreck once m'self; and nigh in another one time when we wuz bound home from Crane's Island in the schooner Sylph. Cap'n wuz anxious to git off early that aft'noon as it looked like narsty weather off to the s'uth'ard, but the dog got ashore and took after some sheep, delayin' us considable.

Wuz wallerin' along off Mother Island when it come up a thick-a-fog, the wind fresh sou'east with a flood tide. We kep on for the Narrers, like dum fools, stead-a goin' out round; got off our course and slid onto Hogback Ledge. It's well out at low water, but the tide bein' high, we wuz a-top of it till a mountin of a sea histed us over. We sort-a coasted down t'other side and made Kester's Harber, leakin' some in the waist, but safe.

'Twuz so quiet in there, Cap'n figgered to tie up side-a wharf, but a current took us aginst it with considable of a bump. The dog, who wuz as fur for'ard as he could git (anticipatin' a little leak of his own, when he got ashore), wuz jounced overboard, and we paddled round and round under the wharf in gloom and fog, with a lantern, mongst a thousand piles (more or less), and fin'lly found the shrivrin' critter aboard a lobster car two wharves away.

13

"Aboard a lobster car"

"Swing ya pardners"

A COUNTRY DANCE

TWO fellers visitin' from Bostin wanted to see some the ole-fashion square dances, so I arranged to go with 'em one Sat'd'y night to a dance in Grange Hall, jest to look on. They perferred to set in the corner by the music, so's to watch Uncle Jake Gilkey fiddle, and thot it "amazin'" that them "big farmin' fingers" could be so spry. Ole Jake is a good-un at it, and cert'nly can saw out a jig on that wire-strung insterment of his when he gits warmed up.

His woman fingered and footed compniments out of her foldin' organ, as usual ("groan-box," Jake calls it). That ole couple had driv eight miles in the fog to git to the hall — rough, narrer roads too, from their place. Jake kep his rubber boots on all evenin', but she had to pump with one shoe off (to ease a corn). Hen Dicksey helped fiddle and ole man Brock, "callin' off" for the square dances, had took out his teeth (to be on the safe side) and hollered so the veins stood out on his neck fit to bust, seems-so.

When it come to "swing ya pardners!" 'twuz fun to see Sid Brock spin a city-bred schoolmarm (here a-visitin'), till the hairpins flew. Then Ed Jergan dared a young squirt from the Center, who wuz a mite lit up with hard cider, to give Ma Creal a whirl. But the rugged ole gal jest gaffled him to her bosom and b'fore he could git into step, spun him till his feet left the floor, shook him loose a-sprawlin' — and he slid half the len'th the hall, flat.

The boys ast me to p'int out the diffrences in the var'ous figgers and steps of each square dance: Plain Quadrille, Pop Goes the Weasel, Bostin Fancy, Portland Fancy, Hull's Victry, Virginy Reel, Speed the Plow, and so on — which I done, best I could.

They seemed to enjoy the dances and ole tunes immense — also the intermission vittles and drink: cider, doughnuts, and cheese.

15

Uncle Jake

Lot and Hank

THE BOATBUILDERS

THERE hain't no better builders of sailin' craft and fishin' craft, no place, than Lot Gilkey and Hank Kester, in my opinion. Neither of 'em had much schoolin'; they learnt about boats — as we all did — by goin' to sea 'fore they wuz half growed, and learnt their trade by workin' with the best boatbuilders up and down the coast.

This is the way they plan a sailin'-craft: Hank whittles away at a small model till it looks right and feels right and balances jest so when he holds his finger under a cert'n place, and Lot — who is purty cute with a pencil — lays out the fine p'ints and dimensions on paper. And when a hull is done, painted and larnched, she'll float at the waterline as acc'rate as any of them ejicated navy artitecs could-a planned her. And all their craft is built on honor: of the best clear, seasoned lumber, and with plenty natural-crook stems, knees, and braces — to give 'em stren'th.

It's fun to watch Hank at a larnchin' — the way he hops round, hollerin' orders and gittin' himself all worked up into a lather.

They wuz larnchin' a thutty-footer one day last fall, and Hank had holt the stern line as the craft started slidin' down the ways a mite sooner'n he'd figgered on, and with considable speed. He wuz yanked off his balance 'fore he could snub the line, but hung on, foolishly, tryin' his best to check her, a-slidin' almost on his back, feet fust, his heels plowin' furrers in the ground.

Into the water went the craft with a splash, Hank still a-hangin' to it — mad stubborn and grittin' his teeth — till his rubber boots sloughed down into some sticky mud.

Waal sir! In a flash he wuz switched end for end and snaked right out-a them boots and into the cold water on his belly.

Mister Alden 'lowed 'twuz "a very entertainin' launchin'."

17

"An entertainin' launchin'"

The Christmas tree

CATTLE

THE only real dairy bizness done in town is at the Dicksie place, run by them two he-wimin, Ella and Mandy. A rugged, able pair of ole maids, they keep eight-ten cows and sell most their milk and butter in Neguntic and to the hotel and summer folks.

Cap'n Deck, next place above theirn, specializes in raisin' and trainin' steers and bulls, and him and the girls has bred some good milk and beef stock with their best critters.

Dexter didn't take up farmin' till he wuz past middle age. Had alw'ys been a sea-farin' man and cap'n of vessels, but havin' a nice famly and bein' wishful to see more of 'em, he decided to come ashore and help his ole man run the farm the rest of his days.

"Navigatin'" a yoke-a steers around is what Deck perfers to do most, but he hollers at 'em so you'd think he imagined himself givin' orders aboard a vessel in a hurricane. No wonder his throat gits sore. He lays his "lung trouble" to gittin' "moon-struck" one night in the tropics, sleepin' bare-chested under a full moon. Shucks! Hollerin's what ails him. But anyways, he can git more work out'f a yoke-a steers than any life-long farmer in town.

Last December Deck come nigh to gittin' lung fever. He'd been up the side of Mount Neguntic with a yoke-a young bulls gittin' out some logs and a Chris'mas tree for the church. It wuz cold enough to freeze two dry rags together, and I callate he sucked in too much zero air, a-hollerin'. But he made out to git over to the Chris'mas Eve ex'cises at the church and hollered some sea chanties for the folks, with a pork poultice round his neck.

Deck's a good neighber and real good comp'ny and the sea lingo he uses in handlin' his cattle is entertainin', but folks can't see no sense in his hollerin' at 'em like they wuz deef.

Cap'n Deck and "the girls"

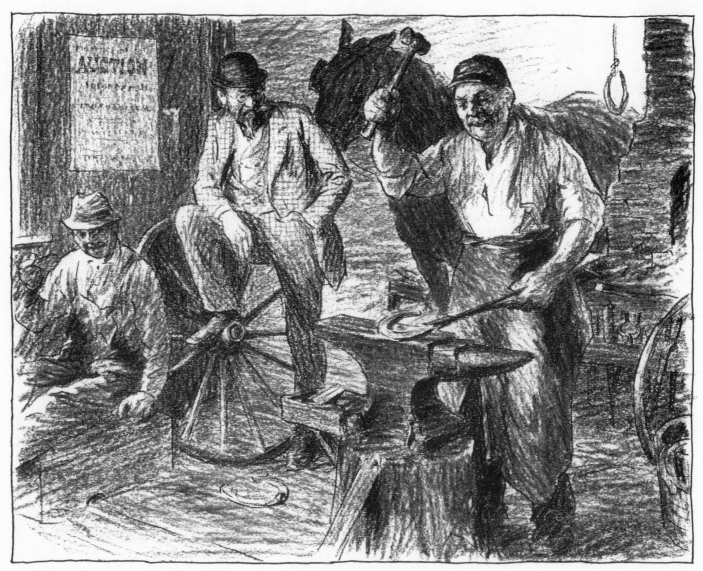

Ike, in his shop

THE BLACKSMITH

IKE'S a jolly critter, a good neighber, a good husband and father, and as able a blacksmith as ever stood at an anvil; and his shop's a place hossmen from far and near like to conregate.

What with hoss-shoein', wagin work, and iron work for boats, Ike has alw'ys been kept purty busy and has prospered. But he never's so busy he won't take the time to do a little job for a young-un: shoein' a sled runner, fixin' a cart-wheel tire, skate, or what not — chargin' little or nothin', or lettin' 'em pay with a chore — and apt as not, Mag, his woman, hands 'em a cookie to boot.

Some folks wonder how Ike ever come to marry Mag, much as a full head taller'n himself, and one-a them hatchet-faced, bleak-lookin' wimin with a tongue that kin scratch glass, most. And yet, strange to relate (or fur's anybody knows), there's never been a cross word b'tween 'em. 'Tween you and me, she takes it out on outsiders or his rel'tives; but if he ketches her at it, he'll say, "Now, now, Maggie," and she'll haul in her sails and calm right down. Ike has as persuadin' a way with her as with hosses.

On their twentieth ann'versry he give Mag as purty a piece of blacksmith work as I ever see: a shovel, tongs, and poker with braided iron-work handles and fancy knobs, for her best-room Franklin stove. And he chuckled when he told me, "She wuz so tickled, she purty nigh looked it, and pecked me on top my head."

One side the shop yard is the most favorite place to pitch hoss-shoes, and Ike kin heave a shoe that's hard to beat. It galls him some that the only one who can beat him most evry time is "Simple Sam." The grinnin' critter will stand there, barefoot, smokin' a "two-fer," hectered by boys, and yet nose out game after game, till Ike comes as nigh to gittin' mad as he knows how.

21

Mag

A "mess o' fish"

A HAND-LINE FISHERMAN

OBIDIAH SMITH takes pride in sayin' the sun never ketches him abed, and about sun-up most evry mornin' — weather permittin' — he sails or rows out to sea "in his dory an' derby," as folks say. Alw'ys wears an ole black derby hat a-fishin'—some claimin' he uses it at times for a bale-scoop or to shock clams into for bait — which is probly jest a story (tho the hat looks gurried up enough).

He perfers hand-line fishin', and knows better'n most of us when and where to git fish. Folks talk about "the poor fisherman," but many a mornin' I've known Diah to run into Bayport with three-four hunderd pound of groundfish. At a cent or two a pound, it 'lows him to take his ease in content the rest of the day. Now and agin he'll hire a hoss and wagin and peddle his fish out back in the country, same's I do — alw'ys figgrin tho to save out aplenty durin' the season to salt down and dry for winter, to sell and eat.

" 'Druther have b'iled salt cod an' pork scraps than beefsteak!" says he (and so say I). And turn up yer nose, if you like, but we "Down Easters" is likewise fond of light-salted dry fish — et raw: "strip-fish" we calls it. It's tastiest when a good hot sun cooks it "cheesy." Awful nice stripped off and et with baked p'taters!

In his younger days Diah fished for some years on the Grand Banks, but ain't been since the last schooner he wuz in, the Jessie Gray, wuz lost with all hands. The last time she tied up in Gloucester, he and his dory-mate went ashore and squandered their share on wimin and other foolishness. The pair of 'em wuz abed in a roomin'-house, drunk, when the Jessie sailed agin without 'em.

And that's the last wuz ever seen of her.

Diah 'lows 'twuz the only time in his life that gittin' drunk done him one mite of good.

23

'Diah

"Jawin' 'round the stove"

THE GENERAL STORE

YOU should see Phil's sketch of Jim — the hair's so natural, slicked (with pepmint flavered porpoise ile), from starboard to port, and the beard all round his mouth bris'lin' off in the same direction from his thumb-wipin' it so much evry time he spits, remindin' me, someway, of one a them wild apple trees by the shore with all the fol'age growin' off to loo'ard from the pervailin' wind.

But, rough as he is, Jim's purty square. He might be guided by his likes and dislikes to "rob Peter to pay Paul" in small ways, givin' good weight and measure to some, and addin' the heft of a finger for others, weighin' a hunk of salt pork wropped in overmuch paper and twine, or none — but on the whole, av-ragin' honest.

Will Tubman's ole 'count books show that licker use to be a considable part of a genrul store's bizness, but since probition, gingy and pepmint extract is all the alchihol they sell. Poison!

But licker or no licker, don't it beat all how much jokin' or jawin' goes on round a store stove? Only t'other aft'noon (that rainy one), they fit the Spanish War all over agin — arguin' 'bout who should git the most credit for takin' Santiago. Si Waley 'lowed that Cap'n Simpson had it all took while Cap'n Shilley wuz thutty mile away (or wuz it t'other way round?).

Anyway, the fur wuz a-flyin' when Dan Gilkey comes in and backs up Jim who wuz givin' Hobson the credit. Then Dan took it up where Jim left off, and (as he gen'ly does) the more he got worked up, the more he swore, till fin'lly, most evry other word wuz a cuss, seems-so — and at last, I'm durned if he didn't split a word in two and tuck a cuss in the middle of it!

Stabbin' a forefinger to'ard Si, he fumed, "All that ails you, Si Waley, is, you're too — too ego — godam — tistical!"

25

Jim, the storekeeper

Inside the mill

THE SAWMILL

YOU might say the sawmill is the heart of Trap Village for the life of the place mostly depends on it. Evry famly has at least one man workin' for John Dasset: loggin', sawin', and handlin' lumber, workin' in the cooper shops and one thing and nother. His family has had the mill privilege ever since his great granfather's day.

Small, nervous, stuttery critter, John, but b'lieves in mixin' fun with work. Forever teasin' ole Andrew who's worked in the mill for three generations of Dassets and donated sevral fingers to the bizness. Andrew snorts and never cracks a smile at John's playful ways.

One hot day some boys who'd been fishin' for eels under the dam peeled off for a salt swim and when they clim up into the millpond for a rinse, John come gallopin' down the log runway — nothin' on but overalls — and dared 'em to see if they could run on the boom logs as fur's he could 'fore fallin' into the water — ole Andrew stoppin' work long enough to snort out of the window.

But like many a small man, John might enjoy his own foolin' and jokin', but wuz apt to be dignified if anybody played a joke on him.

Knowin' his likin' for tinkerin' machinry, Ben Alby come into the mill office one evenin' with an ailin' clock, and ast John if he could fix it. Four-five of us wuz there settin' round. Waal sir! John took them works apart and put 'em together agin all evenin' — cussin' and stutterin' — when, hearin' Jab stifle a cackle, it dawned on him that Ben had brung an extry wheel and slipped it in amongst the mess-a works while helpin' spread 'em on a paper in a chair. John hove a handful of wheels at Ben's head, blowed out the lamps, drove us all out door, tumblin' over each other; and closed up the place with a bang and rattle that set evry dog in the Trap to barkin'.

"Clear out! You-you l-laffin' l-l — loonitics!" he bellered.

John Dasset

"Heavin' the shoes"

PITCHING HOSS-SHOES

NEVER see such a critter for bettin' as Sumner Creal. Jest another one-a the evil ways he's picked up since workin' in Bostin — tho it might-a been born in him, for as a young-un, seems-so he wuz forever sayin', "Well I bet ye!" He'll bet on anythin' under heavens he kin git anyone to take him up on. Go fishin' with him and he'll want-a bet on who'll git the next fish, the biggest, the most — or what kind, with a fine for evry sculpin or such like.

But hoss-shoes is Sumner's specialty — either hove by hand, or as part'f a hoss, tarin' round a race track. When vacationin' here he organizes shoe-heavin' matches and entices folks into bettin' on their favorites aginst him. There's some good uns, and championship matches is held evry year at the town fair. Ed Haskins is good and Ike Woodford wuz champi'n two years runnin'. Then there's Lank Jergan and sevral the boys who throw a ball good also. But as I told you, Simple Sam is a natural jeenous at heavin' hoss-shoes, and would be reconized as champi'n, but for his mind.

A couple of Blue-noses stopped at the Sea View House last summer and had along some quoits — sort'f an iron ring you throw same's a hoss-shoe. They perfessed to be champi'ns. So, Sumner Creal, bein' here, conceived the idee of pittin' Sam aginst 'em, and placin' all the bets he could with the hotel boarders.

Waal, 'twuz quite a show. Sumner got Sam dressed up some and they went at it back of the hotel before a considable crowd. It took Sam a few turns to git the hang of the "quates," and he didn't do too well then till he kicked off the shoes Sumner had lent him.

Then, barefoot, and puffin' a butt he'd picked up, Sam heaved them iron doughnuts onto and aginst the pins till them Blue-noses and all the folks who'd bet on 'em looked sick.

Close work

Lute Frisbie questioning the scholars

THE DISTRICT SCHOOL

I TAKE care of the schoolhouse, and happened to be there t'other day while the school committee wuz vistin', so I set side the wood-pile in the entry and listened to the perceedin's.

Lute Frisbie, the chairman, did considable speakin' and some questionin' of the scholars as usual, but didn't, as usual, entertain 'em 'fore he left by recitin' "Darius Green and His Flyin' Machine" or some other comical pome. A circumstance interfered.

Miss Peevey, the teacher, had had the smartest scholars show off. Some done numbrin' or writin' on the blackboard. Lottie Creal sung "Lightly Roll." Eedie Alby recited a ghost pome, evry verse endin', "and the gobblers'll git ye, if ye — don't — watch — out!" — and, out of mischief, she p'inted each time at the tallest, bashfulest pupil (Lank Jergan's boy), and each time, he'd slide down two-three inches behind his desk — like a clam retreatin' into its shell — till he fin'lly most disappeared.

Then Lute ast for a smart geographty scholar, and Miss Peevey beckoned for Wallie Jubb to stand up. Wallie kind-a dillydallied 'bout it — the only geographty in his memry bein' the location of Lute's best pippin tree, which Lute had ketched him up in, recent. He wuz informin' the school committee that Niagry Falls empties into the Amazon River when little Oscar Dasset raised up his hand, eager.

"Well," says Lute, "p'raps this little man kin tell us right."

'Twuz Oscar's fust day in school. He wuz sett'n behind a post, not in'rested in Niagry, but anxious to show he could do sumthin'. Miss Peevey tho't she'd see what the little feller had to say.

"Hell!" he pipes up, "I bet ye I could shin this post!"

T'other committee man had a chokin' fit and bolted for the door, trippin' over me and knockin' down half the wood-pile.

31

Miss Peevey

" The principal industry "

WHITTLING

A WRITER feller who stopped here a spell ago said it appeared to him that whittlin' wuz one the leadin' industries at Beachmont Village, and I dunno but it does look so sometimes, when evry lounger front the post office and store has his knife out, nickin' or shavin' a stick or a shingle — to no perticler purpose except, as Jim says, "to keep their 'tention off their minds." But you do seem to see the most shavin's after an argyment, and one day Cap'n Deck got so heated he whittled up his ox goad 'fore he realized it.

Now boys, when they whittle, gen'ly figger to make sumthin': a sling shot, willer whistle, or what not. And it alw'ys kind-a tickles me, the serious way they'll try each other's knives and dicker and swap, likewise the names they call 'em by when tradin': "Toad-stabber," "Dabster," "Eel-peeler," "Shaver," and so forth.

But, man or boy, we country Yanks prize a good knife. And yet, the two perseverinest whittlers I know is city bred: Phil and John Hall. They been comin' here summers since they wuz boys. Used to like to whittle boats, and Phil would fuss over a purty one all summer long. He seldom sharpened his knife, but Johnny alw'ys had his knife real sharp and turned out a whole fleet of craft — homely, but staunch. And from that, I perdicted 'bout how them two would turn out in life: Phil becomin' what he himself calls "a poor, putterin' painter," and John prosperin' in commerce.

Both of 'em still like to whittle: Phil, mostly on picture frames, gewgaws, or comical things, and John, on more needful articles. Wuz in the workshop back of John's cottage one day and he wanted me to inspect a "frame" he'd carved, which laid on a box.

"Try it and see how it fits," says he. "Guaranteed to be the comf'tablest, most anitomical privy seat in Jefferson County!"

33

John Hall

The sick cow

THE VETERINARY

BOA'S'N is a purty good hoss, kind and willin', even if he is slab-sided, knee-sprung, parrot-mouthed and wry-tailed, and jest now, 'flicted with a touch of the heaves, from me feedin' him some dusty hay I cut side the road. I should-a known better; 'twuz only fit for beddin'. I'll have to see Will Frisbie and ask him how Doc Peters treated that wind-broken hoss of his.

"Pete" is purty injeenous at doct'rin' critters of all kinds (tho Doc Tibbets swears if he hears of him perscribin' for folks).

"Hell!" says Pete, "I'll admit, critters and men may be muscled and boned into diffrent shapes and wrapped in diffrent kinds of hide, but all have sim'ler innards and ailments — except maybe a few special critter ailments, like barn-itch, seedy-toe and such."

The day he doctered an ailin' cow of Quin Hallack's for stomick-mis'ry — lashin' a gunny-sack of hot mash-turnip up aginst its belly — I told him I'd been troubled with cramps myself. "Stomick-staggers, probly," says he. "Try a turnip poultice on yerself" — which I did, and it done me a power of good.

Yes, Pete truly believes in man-or-beast medicatin' and has quite a follerin'. He wuz raised in Indiany. Says he come east twenty year ago to 'tend a veterinary convention and visit sevral the country fairs — and liked Maine so well he decided to move here.

Saw him t'other day, over to Rube Dunkle's. Rube's pig had the thumps — had been hicuppin' night and day for a week. Pete said it hadn't had ex'cise enough to digest its vittles proper and recommended a bigger pen and a drench of caster ile in warm milk. He stuck the toe of an ole leg-boot smeared with m'lasses into the pig's mouth and poured the dose down the leg, the pig sucklin' it through a hole in the toe, as willin' as a nussin' young-un.

"Doc" Peters

"Cap'n Ben"

COASTING SCHOONER

IT'S a question how much longer Cap'n Ben expects he kin keep that old schooner Nancy afloat. She should-a foundered any time the last ten years. Reglar ole basket! Must-a been built in the same shipyard as the Ark. And yet she still handles most the stuff that's shipped out-a the Cove by water: John's lumber, lime and barr'ls, Hagget's baled hay, and what not. But Ben don't worry none. Soon's she clears a harber, he gen'ly turns the wheel over to his one-man crew and rolls into his bunk with a bottle.

Two summers ago—right after a hold-full of pigs wuz shipped in her from Bayport to Bath—Phil Hall chartered the Nancy to take him and seven city fellers on a cruise mongst the islands for a week. It took considable scrubbin' to 'radicate the signs of the last pass'ngers, but 'twuz done fin'lly (almost), with the aid of a fir balsam smudge. The only sleepin' 'comidations wuz the hold bedded with balsam boughs and hay, covered with a spare sail. "But them dudes seemed to enjoy it, and never belly-ached a mite," says Ben.

In her prime, when Jim Gilkey wuz cap'n of her, the Nancy made trips as fur as Bostin. Done freightin' for Will Tubman, who run the Beachmont wharf-store them days. Will sold considable rum, common rum, but alw'ys wanted the best for himself — which reminds me of a good-un they use to tell on him. On one trip to Bostin, he give Jim an empty jug to git filled with prime ole Medford. Jim put the jug under his bunk and then fergits all about it till he wuz back home. So wha'd he do but sneak into the store, when Will warn't round, and fill up the jug from the common-rum barr'l.

"Here's yer rum, Will," says he, later, in the cabin aboard the vessel; and Will had to take himself a taste, immediate.

"A-ah!" says he, a-smackin', "that's proper rum!"

The Nancy

"Gittin' a hymn tune under way"

THE CHURCH CHOIR

OF late years we shore folks who is more or less pious, ain't been able to hire a parson stiddy, and only hold meetin's at the church when we kin git some revrend to come over from Bayport or Neguntic to fill the pulpit — or when elder Brock offers to preach (tho he ain't what you might call a real licensed parson).

The schoolmarm started a singin' class last winter, and on them Sund'ys when there ain't no preacher, she conducts a sing-service in the evenin'. She also conceived the idee of organizin' a choir to sing at the regler meetin's. Four wuz picked from the singin' class: herself, soprany; Angy Creal, alto; Willard Dunkle, bass, and Jeff Dunkle, tener. Jeff sings a good tener, but is so nighsighted he has to hold the hymn book awful close up, and run his finger 'long the words (and not alw'ys on the right line).

But they sound real good, all told, with Lucy at the melodion (pervided the boy pumpin' it don't let the wind die down, as he did one Sund'y, watchin' a mouse). It's a regler foot-power melodion, but Lucy's feet is so rheumaticy, she had Milt Kester alterate it so it could be pumped from behind by hand.

Parson Dan'lson from Neguntic hated to give up the ole style of church singin': "Brother (so-an'-so), will now lead the conregation in singin' hymn number (such-an'-such)." He seemed to favor Tim Smith for leadin', and Tim would stand up front, wavin' time with a hymn book and beller the words. I kin hear him, and his favorite hymn-tune, now: "From — Green — lan's — ice — ee — mou — n — tins — from — In — jies — co — ral — stra — a — and," with his guttral voice only rangin' up and down three-four notes.

The choir gits a conregation under way with a hymn tune better, to this poor sinner's way of thinkin'.

Lucy at the melodion

The meat cart

MEAT

FUNNY how a man will git into doin' one thing or another for his bread and butter — of'times without no natural leanin' to'ard the thing a-tall. Take Seth Alby; a gentler man never lived — dunno's he ever fired a gun in his life, and wouldn't 'tentionly set his foot on a bug — and yet, he's done the heft the bootcherin' herebouts for twenty years or more. And it's like him, that he alw'ys gits someone to kill the meat-critters he raises himself. Funny!

But on t'other hand, Burke Adams — distant rel'tive of mine who's been drivin' the meat cart for the last two years — is bootch'ry lookin' enough, a red, hairy, bear of a man, the durndest critter for gunnin' and a brute round the house; and yet, he would never hand-bootcher anythin' above a hen, and hates to do that.

Syl Gilkey, who had the meat cart before Burke, wuz better liked. A pleasant, fast-talkin' little man (tho his rithmatic had to be watched). "Now, lessee, Lucy," he might say, "we have six pounds and a quarter of beefsteak at twelve cents? Six t'mes twelve is eighty-four — and a quarter's — waal, we'll call it, say, eighty cents — to you, Lucy."

Syl's idee of a good run-a bizness wuz to help Seth bootcher a beef critter one day, and the next day leave the hide at the tannry and peddle off evry mite the meat b'fore sundown — most b'fore the animal heat wuz out'f it. And he done it, many a time.

But he come to a sudd'n end, poor feller. Heart. Seth got him to bootcher his pig one fall while him and Davy wuz at the fair. Syl got evrythin' ready, as usual — the scaldin' water het, and all — then clim into the pen, stuck the pig, clim out, and dropped dead. And there they found 'em — the pig on one side the fence, and Syl on t'other — laid out, side by side, calm and peaceful.

41

Syl Gilkey

Lon and Frenchy

CORDWOOD

IT takes considable wood durin' the course of a year to keep even one stove like my Trojan Pioneer a-goin' — warmin' my ole bones and heatin' my vittles and drink. I'd alw'ys owned a nice wood lot, so's to be able to cut a year's supply of firewood evry fall — birch, oak, beech, and maple — but needin' some money purty bad one spell, two year ago, I sold it. Since then, I been cuttin' wood on shares some, but lately been workin' up the wreck of "The Alice B." on Alby's Shore, for firewood, at odd times, and manage to git along on that, and what driftwood I kin pick up.

Handlin' an ax sort-a comes natural for most'f us countrymen — tho some is better'n others. The two best choppers I know is Lon Dasset and Frenchy. They make most their livin' at it — cuttin' stove wood, kiln wood, and lumber trees for the mill. Their ways of choppin' is diffrent: Lon takin' a full swing with a regler ax; Frenchy usin' a half swing and quicker strokes with a short-handled, two-bitted ax, the kind with two edges, I mean. They're a good team to have work for you, as each argues as how his way is best — and tries to 'complish more'n the other to prove it.

Speakin' of wood: Skin Jubb landed a load of cordwood at Jim's store a few weeks ago, small stuff, and half of it crookeder'n a dog's hind leg. Skin took his pay and started to hurry off as Jim went out to look it over. But 'fore Skin got out of hearin' Jim called him back — then handed him a quarter extry and a fi'-cent cigar. "Wut's all this for?" says Skin.

"Waal," says Jim, "the quarter is for the extry time you must-a spent huntin' up the smallest, crookedest sticks you could find — and the cigar's a prize for stackin' 'em up into a cord-a wood you could chase a cat through from any p'int of the compass!"

43

"Skin" Jubb

The harness shop

THE HARNESS MAKER

MAY KESTER wuz as han'some and able a gal as a man could ask for, but she had mis'able luck at marryin', poor thing. Her fust man, Eddie Hanson, wuz lost at sea soon after they wuz married. Then she went to Portland and worked at dressmakin' nine years 'fore she wuz spliced to Tom, a harness maker by occipation.

May had done well and had money in the bank. Tom wuz kind'f a sporty feller who'd been takin' her to the races and so on — him in a check suit with a pocket full of cigars, and she, dressed to kill. She fin'lly bought a hoss an' buggy (as a bait for Tom to marry her, I suspect). Anyway, he did, and soon quit his job; then spent his time "ex'cisin' the hoss" and tryin' to make a livin' bettin' on hoss races and cards — with considable drinkin' and sportin'.

Keepin' a hoss and Tom too et up May's bank account so fast she fin'lly lost patience, sold out, and come back to Bayport. Tom follered later and she offered to set him up in a shop if he'd work, and he agreed. They got on well enough; she doin' dress work to home — till pneumony got her. He took to the bottle for comfort.

A good workman, Tom — pickled or sober — and he kin make or repair harness, bags, and other leather goods with the best of 'em (tho an awful numbskull other ways). Jest sets round when he ain't at work, comf'tably stewed, a-puffin' his pipe; his conversation mostly, "God, yes!" or "Dam, no!" — and for other socialty, a visit to a fifty-cent woman down on Dock Street casion'ly.

He took the critter for a drive one summer evenin', and she told of their joggin' along, not payin' much 'tention to the hoss till it took fright at sumthin' and spilled 'em in the ditch.

"Whynt ye 'whoa' him?" says she.

"How could I 'whoa' him," says he, "with the reins in my mouth?"

45

"Dressed to kill"

"Guidin' the team"

FARMING

THERE'S sumthin' comfortin' about seein' a farm well took care of, like Jed Farrer's. I see him plowin' the lower end of his medder piece yist'd'y; little Jappy ridin' the nigh hoss and guidin' the team. The boy is a great comfort to his grampy; has a likin' for livestock of all kinds, and 'druther work with the hosses, most times, than play ordnary young-un's games.

Jed's a mighty good farmer and takes pride in sayin' that none the land his ancesters cleared and stablished for the ole homestead has ever growed up to brush agin. Calls himself olefashion; aims to raise all his own grain and plants quite a piece to wheat — jest as his father and granfather done b'fore him. But since the ole Gristmill burnt, he's had to take his corn and wheat to Edgemont to be ground proper — but his woman 'lows it's wuth it, and "tastes better'n boughten flour and meal." True.

Lots-a places 'long shore ain't farmed as they used to be; the famlies ain't so big, for one thing, and the young fellers drift more'n more to'ard the cities. Jest look at the ole stone walls as you go through the woods; some of them walls marked the bounds of cleared land. Ole Sam Colbert tells of hayin', when a boy, where that well-growed stand of spruce is which he sold, jest recent, to John Dasset, who callates to cut it off next winter, for lumber.

No, you don't see much new land brung under cultivation of late years — tho Jed did stump out an acre or two of that burnt wood lot of his, for p'taters, durin' the Spanish War, when prices wuz high.

He kin still handle a plow, if he is sev'nty-odd.

"Jappy," says he, "why don't me and you show Zack jest how good and straight we kin navigate this plow? I callate 'twould break a snake's back to foller that last furrer!"

Jed Farrer

A "hayrick ride"

SOCIALS

COME to think of it, country folks build considerable many of their good times round the doin' of sumthin' useful: apple parin's, huskin's, quiltin' parties, carpet-rag parties and the like-a that — tho dancin' has alw'ys been pop'lar enough, devil knows.

But speakin' of practical parties, I've been to house-raisin's that 'u'd make any city folks party I ever see look small. Say a feller wuz to build a barn: he'd git the frame together in sections on the ground, and then a raisin' wuz organized, all his men neighbors helpin' raise the frame into place and pin her together. Then his wimin layed out a feast of vittles and drink (a pitcher of rum to one side, maybe), and all hands would fall to. Games would be played later: blind-man's-buff, hunt-the-thimble, spin-the-cover, and so on; follered by dancin' and a good all round sing.

Some the city-folks seem to enjoy our ole-fashion good times — indoor or out — as much as we do. We natives do seem to contrive entertainment enough, the year round, even if we haven't no baseball yard, op'ry house, or Austen-Stones, like Bostin has.

Folks enjoyed the poverty party, give at the Grange Hall, Labor Day evenin'. The last entertainment I went to there wuz an Ole-folks Concert where Miss Peevey organized the singin' of a round, which I sung bass in. It went sump'n like this:

"My dame had a lame, tame crane" (tener),

"My dame had a crane named Jane" (soprany),

"Oh, pray gentle dame, let the lame, tame crane, Jane" (alto),

"Drink — and — come — home — a-gain" (bass), then all together in chorus, back to one at a time, and so, over and over — till Jeff Dunkle fin'lly got the words twisted; his shrill tener pipin' up:

"My crane had a dam lame Jane" — and how evrybudy did howl!

At a "poverty party"

Noontime at the quarry

THE QUARRYMAN

WHEN Phil Hall needs men to set for figgers in any of his paintin's, he likes to hire Blind Carl as much as possible — and time hangs so heavy on the poor feller's hands, he's right grateful for the job.

Carl lost his sight while workin' in the quarries over to Limeford. A spark accidently tetched off a charge of powder he wuz handlin', and it took him right in the face an' eyes. Spent all the money he'd saved, havin' 'em doctored — but 'twarn't no use. Fortunately, his place wuz all payed for, and the town selec'men voted not to collect no more taxes on it. Carl's woman is handy and able and manages to support herself and him, doin' washin' and odd jobs of one kind or nother — often the work of a man.

They come from Sweden, originally, but he learnt his trade up Cape Ann way, in the granite quarries there. Drifted Down East and worked a spell on Monument Island; then come over here — vowin' he wuz tired of livin' on an island "so tam rocky, der cat coot hardly find places to scratch 'erself holes!"

John Dasset hired Carl to take charge when they started gittin' out black granite, over by Juniper Hill. But there didn't prove to be much of a demand for granite that color, so the quarry fin'lly shet down, and Carl took the job in Limeford — only comin' home on Sund'ys, and gen'ly hoofin' it the ten miles, both ways.

He plays the 'cordion awful well, and earns a doller at it now an' agin, to dances. Liked to dance purty well himself, when he had eyes, and 'twuz fun to see him hop down off the platform, loop his arms round a woman (both hands still a-holt the 'cordion), and step into a dance, playin' it behind her back.

Carl wuz alw'ys jolly, and good comp'ny — and still is, despite his affliction, poor feller.

51

"Accordion and all"

Ed's engagement gift

MARRIAGE

I'VE lived in this town now goin' on sev'nty year, and it's been in'erestin', watchin' folks, young and old, pair up and marry, for better or wuss. Been in double harness twice, myself — once for wuss, and once for better. But most married couples seem to be purty content with each other — and I callate nothin' in life is wuth more to a man, than havin' a good woman to stand by him.

My brothers wuz all well spliced: Fred out in Idiho, soon after he went there, years ago. He's only been home once. His woman is an able, jolly critter, but, as Rough Rube Dunkle says, "so homely, 'twould gag ye." And even Fred himself admitted that wimin wuz awful scerce in the minin' town where he met up with her.

Fred wuz sparkin' one-a Rube's daughters 'fore he left home. There wuz five of 'em, all purty. Elizy wuz the oldest, but the last to marry. Married Si Waley, a year after his woman passed on. Guess Si wanted to be sure of gitt'n a ruggeder woman the second try, so he sent Lizy to Doc Adams, to be examined — pertendin' 'twuz for life insurance. Rube wuz tellin' me 'bout it.

"Doc found 'er sound, b'gorry! Wind, limb, and app'tite."

Si's father — widower — took a notion to git married agin, after that. Located a lone widder-woman, in the back-a the town, and started callin'. Her maw door-cracked and lis'ned, and said he'd jest set a spell, sayin' little or nothin', and gen'ly leave a present 'fore he left — sumthin' useful, like 'taters, fish, or clams.

The evenin' he popped the question ('cross the len'th the room), he wuz holdin' a bundle under his arm, and when Nell said, "I jest soon's not, Tobias," he went over and handed it to her.

"Suit-a red underflannels for ye," he grunted. "Good uns! Bran new! Put 'em on an' wear'm!"

53

"Sparkin'"

At "The Sucker Hole"

OLD SWIMMING HOLE

ROWED up to the head the mill pond recent, to cut hoop poles 'long the ole hoss-railway track, and comin' back I stopped to watch a parcel of young scamps at "The Sucker Hole," swimmin' and skylarkin' — jest as us ole fellers use to, when we wuz that age.

The place hain't changed much, and well I rec'lect the summer Uncle Charles learnt me and Freddie to swim. Uncle wuz home from a trip to the Carolinas, as mate in Granfather's vessel. Rough, jolly critter, alw'ys larfin' and jokin', and pop'lar with young-uns. I callate he felt the need of a good wash, so helpin' himself to a bar of Ma's soap, he took us little fellers up stream with him. We wuz 'bout six and eight years old, dressed in jest a shirt and overalls, and Uncle the same, 'cept fer some ole shoes he wore.

Uncle shed the shoes when we come to the Sucker Hole, and wuz givin' Freddie a ride, pig-a-back, when, quicker'n thot, in he dove, off the ledge — Freddie, clo'es and all! They come ashore, Freddie coughin' and blubbrin' and grabbin' Uncle's neck fit to choke him. Then, after layin' out their clo'es to dry, Uncle looked round for me. I wuz up a tree, fur's I could git — but sailers is good at climbin'; he jest clim up and fetched me down, then hove me a-squallin' into the water, end over end, and jumped in after me.

But after we'd went up stream with him a few times, and got the scare out of us, we learnt to swim like a pair-a frogs.

Gorry! Folks, how I wisht I could once agin enjoy the feel of slippin' into the cool water, on a warm summer's day; then stand still, with my feet in the soft mud till the big suckers git over bein' afeared and come bumpin' aginst yer shins. And then, after a good swim, crawl out onto the warm ledge and laze round in the sun to dry off — like I use to, sixty year ago.

55

"Hoop poles"

At the cider mill

CIDER

A POWERFUL sight of apples is run through the ole cider mill evry fall — mostly grummets and windfalls, tho some folks is fussy enough to bring a special apple for their cider: bald'ins, russets or fall porters, or maybe greenin's, kings or sheep's noses.

Cider's nice when it's fresh and sweet, but best, I think, when it's jest startin' to work, and gittin' a mite snappy. A glass of it goes good with some doughnuts and cheese, 'fore you go to bed.

Lots the cider used in this town tho, is sumthin' more than snappy, and I know a few who soak up aplenty of it. Old Put Jergan's the wust. In zero weather, he'll set a keg of it (that's a'ready harder'n sin) outdoor, then bore in and draw off the middle — which ain't friz — and bottle it. I took a taste, once! Godfrey mighty! A glass of it would stun ye! 'Twuz wuss'n the bilge pickle a neighbor of Mat's made, in Vermont: fillin' up a half barr'l of dark maple syrup with old cider and lettin' it alcolize a year.

Taken in modration, or in a mergency, a little stimlant is proper enough — which brings to mind the time, last winter, when Noah Trussel felt obliged to hoof it all the way back to Bayport, after mendin' Jim's store pump. He'd figgered to come and go on the stage, but missed it, someway, goin' back, so made up his mind to walk — tho he knew the eight mile of road wuz most all a glare of ice. But off he starts — after Jim give him a bracer of good old applejack, for luck. Noah told me 'bout it afterwards.

Says he, "I managed to git as fur's Jones's Corner 'fore dark, a-slippin' and slidin' (p'raps Jim's licker help that fur), but the last three mile — from the Corner, home — I felt so beat, it seemed like the seat-a my pants wuz fifty foot astern, loaded with rock, tied to me with a cod-line — and I a-draggin' it!"

"Ole Put"

Indian camp

INDIANS

SOME folks didn't like to have 'em round, but I never could see much harm in an Indian, if you left him alone. Use to see more of 'em years ago, 'fore they stablished the resivation at Oldtown. The Indians them days — and maybe now — seemed to cling to the idee that the country wuz theirs, by rights, and they'd ought-a be 'lowed to squat where they pleased. An odd un might help himself to a little garden stuff, or (without meanin' no perticler harm) scare yer woman into buyin' a birch bark basket of berries — picked, p'raps, in some out-a-sight part of yer own parsture.

They'd come down river in canoes — gen'ly in the spring or early summer — and camp 'long shore, and sevral times, stopped a spell on the flat at the second bend of Trap Stream.

An Indian kin do a neat job-a-work with considable fewer tools than a white man uses, and can't be beat at basket makin', bead work, soft leather tannin' and so on; or at utilizin' natural mateerals, such as birch bark, bone, grasses, and fibres for their work. One day I watched a couple of 'em whackin' the daylights out'f an ash log with the butts of their axes, to loosen the year rings. Then, from cuts they made in the bark, at the end the log, 'bout two inches apart, they peeled off strips, sevral layers at a time, the entire len'th of it. They use 'em to make baskets of.

The critters make a lot-a baskets and knick knacks durin' the winter and use to bring 'em down river to peddle. You'd see one'f 'em trampin' all over town, purty nigh buried in a heap-a baskets. One ole feller had a way of plantin' himself front of yer door, without knockin' nor nothin'; standin' there like a statue, with his eyes shet, chantin' a four-noted Indian tune — till somebudy'd notice him, buy sumthin' to git rid of him, or set the dog on him.

The basket peddler

"Skylarkin' and carryin' on"

SLEIGHING

LAST winter wuz a cold un; the bay friz over down as fur's Cobe's Head, and in mid Janooary they raced hosses on the ice. 'Twuz nice goin' on the town roads too, most the winter, with jest enough snow for smooth sleighin'. And given a good hoss, is there anythin' pleasanter than a sleigh ride, on a crisp, bright, still winter's day, or a moonlight night, with the bells a-jinglin'?

The liv'ry stable has a big pung which they use for sleighin' parties; puttin' two settees in it len'thways, and hay on the floor to keep yer feet warm. One Sat'd'y night Will Frisbie drove a crowd of young folks to a dance in Hilton. They didn't git home till all hours the mornin' — skylarkin' and carryin' on — and wuz singin' "Jingle Bells," at the top of their lungs, as they clim the hill where Holy Tom Titus lives — 'bout two o'clock. He heerd 'em comin' and when they drew abreast, wuz standin' at the winder, in the moonlight, lookin', as Will says, "like one the 'postles, out the bible" — with his long whiskers and nightgown.

Tom raised the winder sash and stuck his head out. "Don't ye know this is the Lord's day!" he hollers; and no sooner said, than that young imp, Billie Tibbets, hove an apple. It only hit the side the house, but Tom drawed in his head and le'go the sash so sudd'n, it dropped down ont' the end of his whiskers.

The young folks didn't realize about it till Tom's woman let it out next day. She said he wuz held like in a trap, with his boney bare knees on the cold, bare floor — kneelin' ("but *not* in a prayin' spirit") — for a considable spell, fumin', and a-fumblin' with the spring winder ketches — 'fore he fin'lly bellered:

"Oh, demmit, Maria! stir yerself out-a-bed, can't ye, and help me free myself — 'fore I free — eeze to death!"

61

"Holy Tom"

"Chucky" and Mother

ROOTS AND HERBS

AN ole character, Chucky Reuben, use to help Mother gather her roots and herbs. He wuz a Cobe, but there bein' two Charles Cobes — descent of Ed and Reuben; distant rel'tives — we diffrentated 'em that way: Charles Ed and Chucky Reuben.

I dunno how Mother got to know so much about nature remidies, but she doctered all our family and half the neighbers of her time.

In helpin' her scour the fields and woods for medicine greejentses, Chucky took in (and made up) considable "root-'n'-yarb l'arnin'," as he called it, and after Mother passed on, he confided to me that if he had his rights, he'd have a shingle hung out and tote a docter's satchel round, "a-treatin' folks consitutions."

"Lis'n," he'd say, "I kin fix what ails ye! Rheumatiz? Chaw some Canady thistle root, like I do. Knocks the creaks an' aches right out-a ye! Never have no more toothache neither. Fever? Chaw the peth of March turnip root. Chills? Try the Thompsonian treatment: red-pepper tea an' dry pepper in yer stockin's.

"Fidgets? Steep some dried skullcap or archangel leaves fer a nerveen. A cold? Lobelia tea mixed with West Injie m'lasses will throw it off (a-vomitin' ye), an' fer a cough take jingshang or spike-root tea, or a cough syrup made of the squeezin's of fir-balsom blisters, or jest water, syrupied with brake root peth."

(Dunno but I'd ought-a hang out a shingle myself — the way I'm reelin' this off.) But Chucky'd run on jest so: "A puffball mushroom to stop bleedin', yaller dock or burr dock b'iled in hard cider is good fer biles (modified with wickyup)," — and so on, no end.

Mother took pains a-brewin' her herbs and roots, but Chucky — bein' shif'less — carried his round in his pockets, and jest chawed 'em raw — and lived to be nigh ninety.

"Nature's remedies"

A baseball quarrel

BASEBALL

WASHIN'TON DICKSEY — with his straw-colored hair and oh-be-joyful whiskers, sportin' a blue jockey-cap on the back'f his head, and standin' five foot three, over all (by most the same a-beam) in barn-door pants with red, fireman's galluses — feels considable puffed up with importance in the midst of a baseball quarrel.

"Don't argue!" says he, in his high voice, "I've seen perfessnul games. I'm empire of this one, and what I decide is final!" He alw'ys app'ints himself empire at the games he organizes, in considration of donatin' balls, bat-sticks and other playin' gear.

Most of the best "Shore" players work in the cooper shops and mill, and any time Wash takes a notion to organize a ball game, it don't take much persuadin' on his part to git 'em to take a half day off. And how John does cuss about "baseball paralyzin' industry." But he gen'ly resigns himself, goes to the game — and is apt to git as excited as anybody there. In fact, after the last game — that made "The Shores" town champi'ns over "The Out-backs" — he put an extry doller in Chet Haskin's pay that week, for battin' in the winnin' home run (tho a cow really helped Chet considable: the fielder who raced to ketch the ball, head up, collided with her).

Wash got wind there wuz a ball team on Harber Island, and sent 'em a challenge. Hired me to sail our team over in The Carrie. We wuz handicapped from the start: Our fastest runner slid into second base on some soft herrin' (strewed on the grass for fertilizer) and finished up the game in a pair of ole sawed off ile-skin pants he borrered. Then, our best batter, in tryin' to git under a high fly-ball in left field, got all snarled up in a fish-net, which wuz spread out there to dry, and hurt his shoulder.

Them Islanders beat us — in spite of Wash empirein'.

"Snarled up"

The lime kiln

THE LIME KILN

THEY been burnin' lime in the ole kiln since Lord knows when, and enough lime-rock to build a mountin must-a been toted from the country herebouts on ox-drags and dumped into it. If you've never seen 'em "draw off" at night, it's kind of a purty sight.

Make a nice paintin'; showin' the men standin' in the light of the red-hot lime as they draw it from the kiln.

The bizness has slacked up some of late years for one reason or nother, but twenty year ago 'twuz hummin'. They even built four mile of hoss-railway to bring lime-rock from a quarry back in the woods to the Trap: spruce rails and iron-wheeled flat cars.

Time was when stone-lime mortar warn't so common, I jedge. The ole Creal house opp'site Holy Tom's has shell-lime plasterin' and the chimbley brick wuz set up in clay. Friends of the Alden's bought the place for a song, to fix up. Stripped the ceilin's to show the original beams, jest as they say 'twuz in sixteen hunderd and sumthin'; then scoured the country, from hell-to-high-water, for period furniture and gear, includin' some-a them bolt-upright, no-rest-for-the-righteous chairs the Pilgrims invented. But in repairin' the clay-set chimbley, they used good "Trap-lime" mortar.

One day Holy Tom wuz over watchin' the worldly perceedin's, and in backin' out-a somebody's way, he tripped and set down in the mortar trough. There warn't much in it, but enough to plaster the seat of his pants in good shape. Mister Alden's friend give him a hand to git onto his feet, and Walt Kester scraped him off.

"I feel considable mortafied," says Holy, mournful like.

But when Mister Alden slapped him on the back and we all roared a-larfin' he stomped home mad, not realizin' that for once in his life — so fur as anybody knows — he had said sumthin' comical.

Lime-rock

Making cheese

BUTTER, CHEESE, EGGS

A rocker churn

THERE wuz a niche seven foot tall at the head the stairs in our ole house, and Mother warn't content till she'd saved up enough butter money to buy a hall clock to put in it. And then one day less'n a year later, we young-uns wuz playin' hide-an'-seek, and when Walter, the littlest, wriggled into the clock to hide, it fell for'ard with a crash and slid the len'th the stairs with him inside.

Mother wuz heartbroke. The wreck of it lay in the attic for years till the summer Phil Hall's father, who liked to tinker clocks, fixed it up as I have it now; goin' good and keepin' time.

In her day Mother wuz considered the best butter and cheese maker in town and Pa let her earn what she could at it. He alw'ys kep five-six cows. Butter, cheese, and eggs wuz as good as cash-money then — and still is, for that matter, tho you don't see so much homemade cheese now. Al Brock's mother's the only one that I know of who makes any. I ast her t'other day how she done it and she said I could help her make one for myself, soon's she could git some rennit — next time Seth bootchered a calf. Nice ole soul, Miss Brock.

Speakin' of eggs — Abbie Dasset (pleasant, timid little woman) come into Jim's store yist'd'y with a basket full — Jim, careless of speech, with a chaw in his cheek nigh the size of an egg, and a dainty habit of thumb-wipin' his mouth after he spits (and has done it so long, the beard all round it sort-a bristles off to the left).

"How much be ye payin' fer eggs today, Jim?" she inquired.

"Twelve cents, Abbie," says he, spittin' and wipin'.

"I'd like awful well to git thuteen," says she, anxious like.

"Sorry, Abbie, but twelve's the price today. I realize it don't hardly pay fer the wear an' tear on the hen's backsides, but twelve's the best we kin do."

69

"Tending the traps"

TWO LOBSTERMEN

THEY ain't never got too rich at it, but Jab and George have been lobsterin' together, off and on, most their lives. They and I kin rec'lect times, years ago, when lobsters wuz so plenty they only fetched a doller a hunderd weight at the cannery. You could often pick 'em up mongst the rockweed 'long shore at low water.

As they got scercer, prices riz, so there's alw'ys been some kind of a livin' in it. We three tried lobsterin' down to Crane Island one year, but them barbarian Islanders cut our buoys adrift and made it so unpleasant for us we had to quit. Like all fishin', you have good luck and bad. Jab and George lost a lot-a traps off the outer shore in that last September line storm; and George's right thumb ain't been much good since he got blood p'ison in it from a lobster pinch and had to go to a Portland hospital to save the hand.

Them two ain't a mite alike; George is so modrit and fun-lovin', and Jab, quick and rattle-headed. I did have to larf one day I see 'em tackin' out the Cove in their sloop; George at the tiller. Jab stood up on the cockpit seat to reach over the side for sumthin' or other with the boat hook, and George come about, cf a-sudden (and a-purpose) at the right time to ketch him on the behind with the boom and dump him overboard head fust.

Jab can't swim, but his head soon come up, spoutin' water and words — "Gh! — sa-ave me!" — then went under agin. Next time it appeared, he gurgled, "Too — late!" shet his eyes and sunk.

George lay to 'longside where diffrent human parts kep showin' nigh the surface, then reached down in and pulled Jab's head out-a water by the hair, and spoke to it, in his modrit way. "Ye might — try — puttin' yer — feet — on — bottom, Jab."

There warn't more'n four foot depth of water above soft mud.

71

George

"Fire!"

FIRES

ONE Sat'd'y evenin', some time before the town pervided us with our twenty manpower hand fire tub, Sleepy Joe Jergan's woman come out to the head the outside stairs leadin' to their rooms over the liv'ry stable, half undressed, a-squealin', "Fire!"

Sure enough, through the winder the place looked all ablaze. Lank Jergan went up the steps, four at a time, and found Joe, in his nightgown and rubber boots, at the kitchen sink pumpin' water into a dishpan. Lank grabbed it, and in his excitement hove the water, pan and all, into the room where the smoke come from.

It seems a draft-a-wind had blew a lace winder curtin over a lamp; it got ablaze and set fire to some papers and culch on a table. 'Twuz out by the time Will Frisbie rushed in to smother it with a wet hoss blanket. Meantime, Joe, daze-eyed and still half asleep, kept right on pumpin' — the water jest goin' down the sink-drain.

'Twuz hard to control much of a house-a-fire them days with only a bucket-brigade, at best, to fight it. Of'times all you could do wuz haul as much stuff as possible out the house and try to keep other buildin' roofs wet to pervent the blaze spreadin'. But nowdays, "The Beachmont Volunteers" haul "Deluge Number 4" to a fire (if 'tain't too fur off). She shows a powerful stream with a good water supply and twenty-thutty men pumpin', turn about, and kin check a fire — pervided it ain't got too great a start.

The experience they had — fust time they tried her out — wuz a mite discouragin'; the night the ole Dagget place burnt to the ground. The men wuz pumpin' away like mad; chief Dicksey hollerin' his head off, "Pump! boys, PUMP! What'n hell ails ye?" — him a-wagglin' the nozzle end of a limp hose to'ard the fire.

(T'other end had been stuck down a dry well.)

73

"Lank" Jergan

At the show

THE MINSTREL SHOW

A NEW boardwalk from the church to the post-office wuz needed, bad. The town couldn't quite afford it, so the Brock boys took holt and organized a minstrel show to help make up the money.

Quite a few folks in town kin perform at one thing or nother, and the Brock boys is jeenuses: Al kin rattle the bones, skuff out a jig, or play the banjo and cornet, and Sid kin sing, fiddle, blow a clar'net, and play a tambrine all over himself.

They practiced for the show at the Grange Hall — so's to be out-a hearin' — and Mason Hall wuz donated for the performance; Sat'd'y b'fore Easter; admission, twenty cents; childen, ten. Most evrybudy went, seems-so, and all 'lowed 'twuz a very enjoyable evenin': good music, good actin', and considable comical jokin'. The end fellers joked about a lot of us ole-timers: told about a birthday party the artist fellers give me, and how I chawed into a sandpaper sandwich, and tried to wash down a mouthful of it with a goblet of beer (which wuz jest jellied tea, topped with beat white-of-egg for froth). "And, ladies and gen'lemens," says Mister Bones, "Zack's teeth and swaller hain't been the same since!"

But Blind Carl got the most clappin' for the effectin' kind of way he sung "Nellie Gray," with his 'cordion for comp'ny. Another hit wuz "G.A.R." Alby, who sung "Dixie" in a gray uniform; and then — while the band played "My Country 'Tis of Thee" — went b'hind the curtin in the dressin' corner and undertook to shift to a blue uniform, so's to sing "Hail Columby." But a sudd'n draft blowed the curtin aside and showed him a-changin' his pants — which ended the show, impromptu, but with the best larf of all. And tho the folks didn't hear "Hail Columby" sung — that's what Aunt Gus exclaimed when she see G.A.R. in his shirt-tail.

"The Brock Boys"

"Uncle Andrew" and his cart

THE TIN PEDDLER

THEM days when Uncle Andrew Muzzey's peddlin' cart use to come through here, the toot of his horn would set wimin-folks to countin' out the pennies in their stockin' to spend for some new tinware or other kitchen gear, or to scurryin' round a-gittin' together whatever he might take in trade — paper, rags and bottles, or maybe salt fish or berries — pervided he had a market for 'em.

Must be 'bout twelve year ago that Andrew took to the road in a little box wagin with a small stock of tinware made by a tinsmith in Neguntic. He done so well, the follerin' winter he had the fancy cart built in which he cruised through the state, up to the time she got stove-up on Trap Bridge. He alw'ys had her painted up in gay colors and kep addin' more variety to his stock each year.

Jolly critter, Uncle Andrew, good at wheedlin' wimin, and alw'ys his fit'nest with a cacklin' flock of 'em round him, him a-jokin' or flirtin' with 'em to git 'em in good humor for bizness.

'Twuz about a year and a half ago, his ole mare took fright half way down South Trap Hill when Mister Alden come out'f his driveway pushin' the high bicycle. The hoss rared and circled, and when Uncle, someway, lost control of the hand brake, she galloped down onto the bridge. The starb'ard front wheel fetched up aginst a stanchion; he landed aboard the hoss, and a shower of tinware, brooms, small trash, a wash b'iler and pails went over the rail and into the water and started for the Atlantic with a fair wind and tide.

And right then and there Uncle Andrew decided to retire from bizness. He sold the wreck of his cart to Milt Kester and swapped a mess of stock with Jim for an ole carryall.

He's been livin' over Augusty way on a little place, and there ain't been a tin-peddler through here since. We miss him.

77

Tinware

One sailing party

SAILING PARTIES

MY ole center-board sloop, Carrie, is a good un for sailin' parties; beamy, so shaller draft she can make any port wetted by anythin' from an ocean to a heavy dew (figgertively speakin'). And yet, she's plenty able in a stiff breeze-a-wind and heavy seas. Hank Kester built her 'fore he and Lot Gilkey organized their boat-yard, but she's still sound spite'f all the years that's on her.

Nothin's much pleasanter than a sail to some purty island for a picnic and clam bake with a boat load of folks who don't fret whether we're driftin' with no air except up and down the mast, or weatherin' a gale, the lee rail under, and evrybody soaked with spray.

No better place to jedge folks's natures than aboard a small craft when the weather's narsty. The belly-achinest party I ever took out wuz a little whipper-snapper docter and a square-shouldered nurse he wuz goin' with, his pa and uncle and two ole-maid aunts and a nephy they wuz lookin' after while his ma wuz confined.

We had anchored in Sheep Island Cove to go ashore, and one-a them ole girls, in backin' over the side into the tender — while the doc wuz tryin' to hold it 'longside — swung it off; and there she hung, stretched out, her hands grabbin' the Carrie's rail and her toes hooked into the tender, the front'f her dress in the water.

I grabbed her by the seat'f her skirt and histed her into the cockpit on all fours. But all the thanks I got (soon's she quit tremblin' enough to talk) wuz to be jawed for handlin' her so.

Comin' home we run into a nasty squall off Hurricane Head. The nurse kep cool enough, but the menfolks fretted some; and the two ole hairpins gaffled holt of one another and plumped down onto their knees, prayin' for "deliv'rance from desaster!"

Shucks!

The Carrie

"Forever a-tumblin'"

THE CARPENTER

'TWUZ in the fall of eighty-six my house burnt down. The wife's doughnut fat got afire and in tryin' to put it out, some of it flamed into the woodbox and she come outdoor a-hollerin'. I wuz out on the water at the time, and when I got ashore there warn't much left, except what household gear they managed to haul out.

But Tom Kester got busy and organized a crew-a men who took holt, cleaned up the mess and had a new buildin' framed, shingled, and cla'boarded 'fore snowfall.

Tom was a hus'ler if there ever wuz one, but there warn't many that liked to work for him, he crowded you so. He probly put together more lumber, brick, and stone than any three avrage builders. A rough workman maybe, but anythin' he did put together, stayed put. "Hammer-finish carpentrin'," Milt called it — and some truth in it, for Tom was apt to sink the head of his hammer right in after the nail; on finish-work, cuffin' a little spit on the dent to swell it out, if he warn't in too much'f a hurry. But he gen'ly was in a hurry, and so careless, he wuz forever tumblin' off sumthin' or gittin' bashed up otherways.

Hurry fin'lly finished him at sev'nty: 'cute indigestion. Livin' alone, and bein' in a hurry to git to a job one mornin', he mixed up and et a bowl of dry cornmeal, raisins an' milk.

About nine o'clock he begun to swell.

Lute Frisbie, who layed him out, said he never see such a self-tinkered human body: from the braces holdin' Tom's twisted foot, and the break in his left arm — which had healed with gris'le in place of bone — to his "patent rupture resister," not to mention one'f his teeth, which he told me on his last birthday, still held an 'east-cake-wrapper fillin' he'd tamped into it ten year a-gone.

Tom Kester

Wet hens

PIGS AND HENS

PIGS and hens seem to pervide the heft of the meat vittles for a good many of us country folks and as for pork, I figger it's probly et in more diffrent ways than any other eatable critter. Most of us callate to raise and kill a pig or two evry year; eat up the fresh loin and otherways work up the rest for the winter: ham, salt pork, sausage, lard, etcetery.

Alw'ys liked to have a few hens peckin' round the place too. A b'iled hen is a good change from pork and fish and 'long with eggs, for quick vittles, helps keep our consitutions in workin' order.

Speakin' of pigs — you'd larf to see young Davie Alby sky-larkin' with a pig his pa give him to raise; as much of a pet as a dog. Half grown now but Davie will still wrastle and roll round with him in the little "pig pasture" he fenced in — both a-squealin'.

Nice young-un, Davie. Alw'ys makin' a pet of sumthin'. Has a little flock of hens of his own and wild critters in cages stuck round in the sheds and barns: a screech-owl, turtle, duck, chip-munk, and what not. Full of pranks he is too but don't mean no harm. I made the mistake of tellin' him of some the mischief my younger brother, Walter, use to play on farm critters when we were young-uns together and 'twarn't but a day or two after he thot up a piece of devilment of his own — purty injeenous it was too.

He deepened a holler place in the ground, back of the wood-shed — 'bout six foot across and ten inches deep — and filled it with water. Then he scummed over the water and the dirt round it with chaff — so it all looked like solid ground — scattered some corn over it all, banged on a tin dish and called the hens.

I happened in jest as Davie wuz squealin' with glee at the sight of them hens gittin' an unexpected duckin'. The scamp!

Davie and Squealy

The Spiritual meeting

CAMP MEETING

I'VE a suspicion that lots the day visiters to the campgrounds durin' the meetin's go mostly for a picnic dinner — tho they might feel duty bound to set through the service fust (and if it's Methdist, only to git threatened with hell-fire an' brimstone for not repentin' the good times "Ole Nick" pervides his custermers).

Rowed up to the Spiritchul Grounds last year and went into their meetin', out-a curos'ty. Happened to set by John Hall. A blindfolded woman wuz on the platform readin' a message from a "stout, dark-complected" she-spirit who wanted "John" to know that "evrythin' wuz beautiful!" I nudged John and he p'inted out two-three other Johns who appeared to be competin' for that message by sheddin' a tear or two. "The true believers" settin' up front seemed to git the most messages. Beats tel'graphin', no wires nor nothin'. But jokin's aside, I'm glad if it gives 'em any comfort.

Spent the aft'noon at the Methdist Grounds and et supper with my brother Al's family on the shore. When we wuz all set, he, bein' pious, started to bless the vittles:

"Heavenly Father," says he — "Where'n the world is the squash pie?" says his wife, interuptin' — and when Al opened his eyes, kind-a startled, she sent their boy, Walter, to the buggy to look for it. I 'lowed 'twould be too bad if 'twarn't blessed and sujjested includin' the hosses oats (jest in fun). She tightened.

Young-un like, Walter come back carryin' the pie on top'f his head; stumbled, of course, and dropped it, bottom up, on the gravel beach. Al mentioned the Lord agin and cuffed the little scamp. And then (bein' one that hates waste), he slithered an ole shingle under the pie, flipped it over, and him and the wife picked out pebbles till 'twuz fit to jine the other vittles and be blessed.

Little Walter

The double sled

COASTING

WE had a lot-a snow the winter Uncle John Kester come up from the West Injies for a visit. Fust time he'd been back home since he quit his vessel in Trinidad when he wuz in his early twenties. Been workin' there ever since; tradin' and one thing and nother.

He says it avrages purty warm in that part the world, and I thot it strange he should choose winter time to visit back here. But he didn't seem to mind the cold so awful much, and appeared to enjoy gitt'n out and helpin' with the chores. Said Maine air and vittles give him an app'tite he hadn't had since he wuz a boy.

Liked to talk with us who growed up with him 'bout the good times we use to have: skatin', snowball fights, pung ridin' to dances; and how he beat the coastin' record for distince, slidin' from the top the rise on Bare Mountin road to the Cove, over the bridge, down Crow P'int Lane onto the ice and over to Iron Island.

John wuz over to Bay View Hill watchin' a lot-a young-uns coastin' one aft'noon. For fun, he ast Hoddie Dicksey for a ride on his double-sled — half meanin' it, I callate, for it didn't take much persuadin' on Hoddie's part to git him aboard.

Waal sir! The dev'lish old fool not only tried it once, but fergot his age and clim that hill much as six-eight times to git a ride down. Got so in'rested, he tried it the last time alone, settin' on a single sled he borrered; undertook to steer with his heels, and wound up in a snowdrift, side the road — snow up his pant-legs and sleeves, in his whiskers and down his neck. But he jest larfed with the boys while they helped him gather himself together. Ketched an awful cold from it and wuz creaky and lame as an old hoss for a few days — but he 'lowed 'twuz wuth it.

"Sumthin' ye can't do in Trinidad," says he, snifflin'.

87

"Uncle John" Kester

A lumberjack fight

LOGGING

THEY been haulin' logs out the woods herebouts from the time Maine wuz still a part of Mass'chusetts, and yet you kin alw'ys find good stands-a timber, in places; not much real ole growth, tho Phil did trudge me in to see a piece he discovered. He'd noticed some big pines, fur off aginst the sky, lookin' sou'west from Josh Ingram's upper parsture, and got himself lost half a day findin' 'em. They wuz at the head of South Trap Brook, on a knoll surrounded by cranb'ry bog, and them trees wuz ole whoppers, sure enough. We see a hawk chasin' a squirrel round a trunk more'n five foot through; forty foot, I'd say, to the fust limb. Only the up-an'-down saw that wuz in the ole mill could've ripped it.

Years ago I chopped one winter up in Somerset County. Cold? Cr-acky! They wuz times when "cookee" went round at noon with the pail of pork an' beans, 'twuz a hus'le to wolf 'em off yer plate b'fore they friz solid. A rough an' rugged life, but I liked it. Now and agin there'd be a fight for entertainment. And when two or a gang of angry knot-heads started workin' on each other with such weepons as spike boots or peevey handles, the boss had to git out his medicine book and look up some repairin' idees.

But the evenin's in camp wuz cozy — tho you fresh-air fellers might've thot the low-studded bunk-room, crowded with men, a mite stuffy, if you wuz to step in from, say, thutty below outside to eighty above, or so, inside; the place blue with tobaccy-smoke, and steam from sweaty shirts and wet socks a-dryin' out.

And come spring, when the men finished up drivin' the logs down river, a swarm of them woods-wild idiots would romp into Bangor and squander their winter's wages in a few nights.

Licker, cards, and "calico"!

"Ole whoppers"

"Whistlin' for a breeze"

SUPERSTITIONS

LOTS-A folks is so superstitiony they kin hardly turn round without seein' or hearin' sumthin' to make a sayin' over; either warnin', perdictin', lamentin', or rejoicin'. Most wimin appear to be more so than men, I'd say, tho sea-farin' men ain't fur behind.

Some of our sailer superstitions? — oh, fool idees like, whis'lin' up a breeze, callin' it bad luck to kick the ship's cat overboard in anger, or losin' a bucket or mop overboard; and sayin's like, "shower in the mornin', sailer take warnin'; shower at night, sailer's delight"; or believin' ye're apt to die b'fore the end the voyage if the full moon should shine on yer face in bed — and so on.

But ole wimin is the wust. You should-a heerd Gram Dunkle and Rube's woman arguin' one day over cookin' a corned haddock.

"See them black stripes down the side the critter?" says Gram, "where it slipped through the devil's fingers?"

"Nonsense!" says Kate, "'twuz Saint Peter that had holt of it!"

"Waal, if he did, the devil tried to grab it away from him and tainted it!" says Gram. "Ye don't ketch me eatin' none'f it!"

Kate fin'lly had the last word and left the room, a-whis'lin'.

"Whis'lin' women and crowin' hens don't never come to no good ends!" Gram croaked after her.

I stepped out to see how Rube wuz gittin' on with the new privy he wuz finishin'. He wuz holdin' a hoss-shoe up aginst the door, speclatin' on whether it should hang p'ints up or p'ints down. He fin'lly made it fast, p'ints down, and went in to chris'n her. I heerd him "tie-dee-oodlin'" to himself as I went back into the house and Gram inquired who wuz singin' and where. I told her.

"Whis'le or sing in a privy will bring bad weather, sure thing!" says she, dismal like.

Gram Dunkle

An auction

THE AUCTIONEER

'TWARN'T more'n a month or so after her man's fun'ral that the widder Rawson auctioned off most of her household goods and went to live with her brother over Waterville way.

She knew Nat wuz spoke for nigh a year 'fore he got through — as we all suspected — includin' that forehanded critter, Gabby Jones. Seems-so Gabby wuz alw'ys right on the tails the undertaker when a woman wuz left a widder. I wouldn't go so fur's to say he ever actually persuaded 'em to auction off their worldly goods, but you must admit he done well by them who did. As Will Frisbie said once, "He could sell a fiddle to a one-arm deef an' dumber," and for a fact you did have to look out he didn't mesm'rise you into noddin' yer head to raise the bid on sumthin' you warn't a mite in'rested in.

But he was an entertainin' critter a-doin' his job. At the widder's sale there wuz a mess of tools and paint Jab Tubman wuz anxious to git, and Gabby had him so worked up he got to biddin' aginst himself and paid fifteen-twenty cents more'n he needed to.

When they auctioned off what wuz left in the old Hagget house, Phil got holt of some ancient trash from the attic — ole clo'es, chests, books and things, for his city stoojo, he said; also some bottles, jugs, and brass stuff, for "still life" (whatever that is).

Poor ole Gabby! The last time I see him at work wuz jest a month b'fore his mind failed and he had to be put away. He wuz persidin' at an auction for the ben'fit the ole Center church, and never did appear in better shape; had evrybudy in roars with his mimicin' of all kinds-a fereign folks and animals.

I'd like to see him once agin, standin' on a sea-chest in his fancy clo'es, lecturin' with len'thy words on the virtues of some wheezy, wind-broken melodion, or sway-legged privy chair.

"Gabby"

A "salmon berth"

SALMON FISHING

THEM that own property adjinin' to the shore here is as much fishermen as farmers, as a rule — specially at salmonin'. And in the season when they're runnin', from April to July, you'll see a few or more "hook-a nets" moored in the water opp'site most evrybudy's place that has a frontage on the shore.

This bay has alw'ys been a good un for salmon, it bein' at the mouth of one-a the best spawnin' rivers. 'Fore the mill wuz where it is we built a fish-way there, to entice salmon to go up Trap Stream to spawn; but it didn't work out too good for some reason.

Salmonin' takes considable more gear and fussin' than most other kinds of fishin': carin' for the kind-a complicated net-traps; repairin' 'em, dyein' 'em, and keepin' 'em free from weed, drift-wood, and trash when they're in use. But then, salmon's a fish that fetches the best price of any, and in the Bostin market they consider them from this bay the best that can be had.

Naturally, other fish git into the salmon nets also: pollock, cod, and now'n agin a blackfish or porpoise; and once, when I wuz fishin' with Jab, we got a baby seal, and I made a pet of him round the fish-house. Brung him up on the bottle. But my dog Snap got jealous and pestered the little critter so, that when I had him well weaned, we took him over to Dog Island Thorofare, where there's so many seal, and turned him loose.

Old Jud Creal and Linc Alby tell of a time they got a two-hunderd and eighty-five-or-so pound sturgeon in their salmon nets (tho the fish's heft and other details vary more or less in the tellin' as the years roll on, I've noticed). But b'tween 'em they kin make quite a yarn of it (specially if their tongues has been well loosened with a little red-licker). And evrybudy

Linc and Jud

95

agrees, 'taint told right unless they do do it together.

Phil Hall had me and them over to his cottage one evenin' so a writer feller could hear it. Linc begun the tellin', as usual.

Says he, "When me an' Jud rowed off that mornin', we wuz aware of a big fish in the head net soon's we started haulin' and 'twuz much's the two of us could do to git enough-a the net into the boat to see him, he thrashed round so. But fin'lly, through the foam an' spray I see 'twuz a sturgeon, an' a whopper. I managed to git the gaff into him, but he'd-a pulled me overboard if Jud hadn't grabbed my legs. Hurt my side dre'ful on the gun'le the boat!"

"Nigh overboard"

Then Jud hitched his chair for'ard and took up the story.

"Waal, I managed to git Linc back into the boat, wet down-t' the waist, and dizzied by a cuff side the head from the sturgeon's tail, but still grippin' the gaff till I took holt and made out to stun the fightin' critter with my salmon-killer.

"I rowed ashore, towin' it — Linc takin' on terrible 'bout his side meantime — an' had it dragged half way up the boat slips when it come to life and tail-swiped Linc off his feet. So I had to stun it agin 'fore draggin' it the rest the way up to the fish house. After it quit gaspin' I perceeded to dress it."

"Tail-swiped Linc"

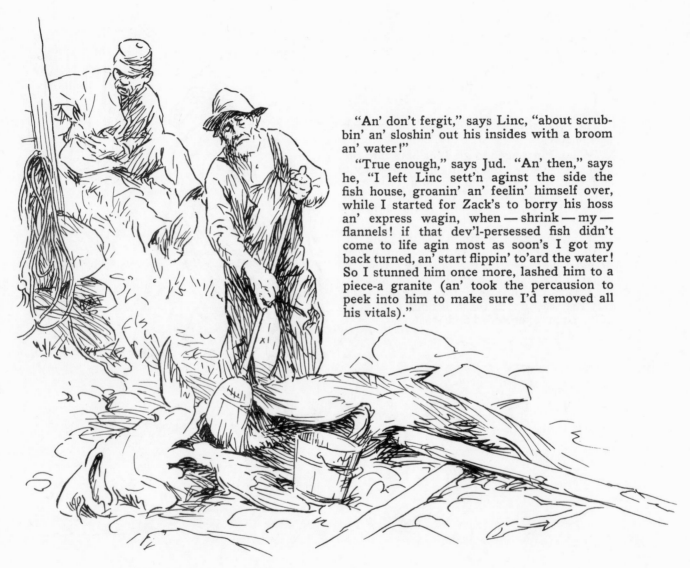

"An' don't fergit," says Linc, "about scrubbin' an' sloshin' out his insides with a broom an' water!"

"True enough," says Jud. "An' then," says he, "I left Linc sett'n aginst the side the fish house, groanin' an' feelin' himself over, while I started for Zack's to borry his hoss an' express wagin, when — shrink — my — flannels! if that dev'l-persessed fish didn't come to life agin most as soon's I got my back turned, an' start flippin' to'ard the water! So I stunned him once more, lashed him to a piece-a granite (an' took the percausion to peek into him to make sure I'd removed all his vitals)."

The "stunned" fish

"Waal, to make a long story short," says Linc, "when Jud had come back from Zack's with the rig an' unlashed the fish (after makin' sure there warn't a twitch left in the critter), he perceeded to load the two bodies — me an' it — aboard the wagin an' headed for Bayport — goin' slow an' easy on 'count of my suffrin's.

"We wuz joggin' along — comf'table's could be expected under the circumstances an' conditions — when, about a third the way to town — I swan! — if that horny-plated hell-fish didn't fetch me one last slat with his tail! — a-knockin' me right over the dashboard in amongst the hoss'es hind legs — head down!"

"One last slat"

"In the end," says Jud, "the doct'rin' of Linc's busted rib an' strains took all the money we got for the durn fish. But that day in Bayport he felt so low, 'fore we started back, I bedded the wagin body with hay, an' me an' Doc laid him in caticorner-ways. Yet, he cussed an' complained so stiddy the whole ten miles home, I had to stop an' water him two-three times — his mouth got so dry.

"I'd brung back a sizeable chunk off the tail-end the fish to devide with Linc, but he warn't in'rested a mite; jest turned his face to the wall, a-groanin' some words which I 'terpreted to mean 'No app'tite for sturgeon, perticly the tail end of that one'!"

"Cussin' an' complainin'"

Then Jud an' Linc took turns goin' back over the yarn, tetchin' it up here an' there an' "jes' so"-in' each other's additions.

At the end, Phil, as a reward for their efforts in tellin' this truthful tale, held up the bottle invitin' like, an' both to once said they didn't mind if they did have another "li'l taste"; "but not no gingy ale in mine!" says Linc. So Phil poured him out a good un (which he gulped down a mite too eager an' coughed an' choked so the tears run). But he sniffed, blinked, an' "hemmed" till he found his voice, then cockin' his head sideways, perlite, he wheezed in a weak, quavery falsetto, "N — n-nice — thankee."

"N-n-nice--thankee"

Cooking day

COOKING

WHAT a grist-a vittles my good mother did use to turn out in the ole kitchen day after day for our big famly. And on Sat'd'ys, 'twuz 'bout all she did: bread, brown bread an' beans, pies, cookies, doughnuts — maybe with young-uns underfoot teasin' for the sweet-dough bowl and mixin' spoon to lap out. "Don't scrape it so clean, Ma!" we'd whine, jest as my gran-childen do today.

I callate Yanks eat more sweet vittles than most nationalties, and with evry meal. Never had much'f a sweet tooth myself, but did like my last wife's "apple grunters": a deep pie, seasoned with fat pork and m'lasses. But Uncle Enos is the durndest hand for sweets, specially sass. Any meal he don't see none mongst the vittles, he'll say to his sister, "Where's yer sass, Sis?"

"Sis" ain't no great shakes of a cook, but one summer John Hall inquired if she'd work at their cottage. "Well," says she, "I dunno's I know too much about cookin' (and what I do know, I hain't so sure of)." But she tried it a week or two — till John's famly and comp'ny quit tryin' to like her ole-fashioned messes: "pork pie," "coosh haddle," "blueb'ry slump," "bumblicue," "cod frizzle," and such like.

Most wimin is able enough cooks — and some men (tho I've alw'ys been an awful gorm at it). One day when I wuz livin' and guidin' with the Perfesser at Camp Porky, I tried to contrive a mess-a doughnuts out-a pancake dough. They riz fine, but with each one I fried, the fat in the fry pail sunk half-a cupful, seems-so. Nev'theless, the Perfesser, eager like, et two-three, hot — the grease runnin' down the corners of his mouth into his whiskers.

Purty soon he started pacin' back and forth, kind-a hunched over and anxious-eyed, his mouth openin' and shettin'. Fin'lly, he had to lay down (and warn't a mite sociable till next mornin').

103

"Sis"

The Beachmont Brass Band

THE TOWN BAND

IT wuz organized and is still led by Al Brock. Him and his brother had alw'ys played cornet and clar'net, but most the boys in town who had a leanin' for music, fiddled. But some wuz willin' to take up wind music, so they got together a fund of money — one way and another — and Sid Brock went to Portland to see what he could do in the way of findin' the insterments that wuz needed (second-hand ones), specially the big horns and a bass drum. I donated a snare drum which my brother Charles used durin' the Civil War.

The beginners on the diffrent wind insterments made fust-rate progress; tho them that practiced on the big horns round the house warn't much of a comfort to their famlies I imagine — Billie Alby, with his trombone, f'rinstance: his gramp allowed it reminded him of a weanin' calf bellerin' into a tin feed pail.

But Al brung 'em all together at the Grange Hall often as he could for practice, and fin'lly built up a real smart band. They played in public for the fust time at the Edgemont fair. One feature of that fair is the squirtin' contest between the hand fire tubs from the diffrent towns. Our village entered ole "Deluge Number 4" — and durned if our boys didn't win, with the band standin' by and eggin' 'em on; playin', "Johnny Git Yer Gun"!

Since then the "Beachmont Brass Band" has played a lot, here and there: for cel'brations, fairs, ent'tainments, dances, and what all. They wuz in the perade at the county seat last Fourth July, and looked real smart in their new uniforms: hat, coat, and belt — all but that ganglin' Waley boy who blows the piccerlo. He flapped along in some white canvas pants (some feller from the city had give him, roomy enough for two of him) which his ma had starched and creased crossways, stead of fore an' aft.

105

Practicing

"Twuz fun to see 'em"

TRADING

A WELL liked dealer in livestock is Asa Dicksey in Neguntic.
But his pardner, Mark Corbett! — I think if it warn't for
Asa that snide would be a-pickin' oakum behind bars.

Mark travels round tradin' or buyin' anythin' under heavens
and you're liable to see him towin' a string of farm animals, or
with a wagin load of household gear, or maybe jest a carpetsack
full of knickknacks and jewlry. Durndest critter! More'n once
Asa has made him square things with some lone widder woman
he'd snided out'f a nice carriage, a barn-full of hay or p'raps some
cherished heirloom — dazzlin' her with a loose roll of one-doller
bills or offerin' to trade a fancy piece of furniture — out of a
catalogue.

Ing Small, stock farmer, out back, bested him bad once tho.
Him and Mark had done bizness at odd times without either
gittin' bad bit. 'Twuz fun to see 'em at it. Ing would fetch out
a critter he wanted to sell or trade. "Thar's a hoss!" he'd say,
"sound! wind, limb an' pizzle!" then draw himself up to his full
six-foot-four and "humph!" and spit while Mark picked flaws in
the critter.

"Waal! What kind'f an ole sag-belly have we here!" Mark
would groan. "Le's look at his teeth (if he has any) an' see."

The trade I set out to speak of: Mark traded a good old mare
and wagin with Ing for a smooth and purty but narsty-tempered
four-year-old which at the time of the deal wuz gentle and perky
as a kitten.

Mark wuz drivin' home on a pair of old front wheels rigged
with a board and blanket, purty content with himself, when the
critter's personal'ty come back: he kicked himself clear of Mark
and the rig and run wild in the woods for six days 'fore they
got him.

At the time of the trade, Ing had mollified the critter by pourin'
a bottle of that thutty percent Solomon's Sasparilli with some
sugar into its drink pail while Mark wuz nosin' round the cow
shed.

Mark Corbett

Hiram, at work

THE SAIL MAKER

I'M runnin' up to Neguntic in The Carrie this mornin', and would be glad of comp'ny if anybudy feels like goin' along. There's a fair wind and the tide 'll faver us both ways. Phil Hall's friends hired the craft t'other day to go over to the islands, and I callate their weather eye must-a been to loo'ard when a little squall slapped her comin' out of Pocket Harber and the mains'l ripped when she jibed. We'll have to sail with a double reef in her, but if the wind holds the way 'tis we ought-a make purty good time.

Waal, Hiram 'll patch it for us. Met Hiram? No? He opprates Gould's sail loft — been there ever since he wuz a 'prentice fifty year or more ago. We wuz boys together. He stutters terrible but is probly the best all-round sail maker on the bay. There warn't many sewin' machines used in sail makin' — at least up this way — until late years, and Hi must-a pushed and yanked a sailer's needle through enough canvas to blanket the state-a Maine.

When the last man, Gould, died, Hiram took over the bizness from the widder; and while tain't what 'twuz when vessels wuz bein' built in evry tide puddle 'long the coast, there's still enough orders to keep him busy — as well's that young calf (step-son of his) he's tryin' to larn the bizness to. It's amusin' to hear Hi sputter when the boy don't do sumthin' jest right, tho he's really fond of him, never havin' had no childen of his own.

Last time I wuz into the place he'd sent the youngster to the hardware store for some grummets or sumthin' he wanted in a hurry, only to have him come back with the wrong sizes or kinds.

"Edward," says Hi, "if the b-brains wuz took out of that m-um-m'mess of bone b'tween yore ears, 't-twouldn't lea-leave a cav'ty b-big 'nough for a p — p-p-p — pismire to turn round in!"

109

Edward

The "faintin' party"

THE COUNTRY DOCTOR

I DON'T callate anybudy does more real good than a country docter, answerin' calls any time of day or night, winter or summer, sometimes a-hossback or a-foot if the goin's too bad to git out a rig, and, pay or no pay, fetchin' young-uns into the world or comfortin' old uns on their way out; alw'ys aimin' to free folks from their aches and mis'ries or maybe snatch some ailin' soul from the brink-a the grave, who'd dosed himself with a cure-all. As Doc Tibbets' missus says: " 'Twould be a harder life than it is, if there warn't amusin' happ'nin's to chirk us up." Doc told me 'bout a "faintin' party" he 'tended out to Slab City one evenin'.

Hud Haskin's woman had sent for him to haul an achin' tooth. Lil's a hefty woman, but awful scarry, and soon's Doc tucked her head under his arm, with Hud holdin' a lamp, she says, "I know I sh'll holler!" and did, soon's he ast her to open her mouth "wide." Then the light begun to wabble and Hud, pale's a sheet, shuffled and teetered back'ards in a faint. And when Lil see him she fainted, and her sister (eyein' a door crack) fainted when she see the lamp chimbley smash and Lil fallin' one way and Hud t'other.

Doc le'go of Lil to go haul Hud out'f a kittle of hot hog vittles he'd tripped and se'down in (b'iled swill an' corn mush), then he sp'iled his coat smotherin' a blaze of ile where the lamp had fell and busted. Meantime, Hud had come to. So Doc told him to souse the wimin with cold water, and then he left for home in disgust.

But a half mile on he stopped his hoss to have a good larf, then went back to see how things wuz. The wimin wuz up and around, but Hud wuz abed, face down, lookin' mis'able. He inquired of Doc if fresh butter warn't a good salve for "scalt hide," complainin' that he "never could" sleep on his stomick, "ever!"

A winter call

The bean hole supper

BEANS

I FIND that most folks who has et 'em agree that no beans taste so good as them baked in the ground. And for that reason me and Jud built us a bean hole some years back so we could enjoy a mess now and agin, like we use to when we wuz up in the big woods. You know round a lumber camp a belly full of beans with plenty salt pork has alw'ys been considered powerful good ammunition to handle trees on in cold weather.

Dunno how the custom started of havin' oven-baked beans special for Sat'd'y night supper and Sund'y breakfast, with brown bread and pie, but that's how most'f us likes 'em. One Sat'd'y last fall the Trap wimin got up a harvest bean supper and thot 'twould be "cute" to bake the beans in our hole. So Jud got out the ole iron pot the day b'fore, and while his woman made ready to load her with the regler 'greedientses: parb'iled "yaller-eyes" and water, salt, salt pork, m'lasses and mustud, we built a fire in the hole, and b'fore bedtime buried the pot, with the cover clamped on, in the hot rocks and coals with a coverin' of earth.

Sat'd'y evenin' bein' mild the folks thot 'twould be gay to eat by the bean hole, and all vowed they'd never tasted such beans. Seth Alby brung his own eatin' knife, as usual. He claims he can't enjoy his vittles with no other, at home or visitin'. It's all wore down narrer and nigh sharp enough to shave with, but it beats all how he kin shovel in beans without losin' any or drawin' blood.

After supper, I remember we all felt like visitin' t'gether a spell, but Jud made an infernal racket in the shed 'longside, thrashin' out a new kind-a bean he wanted us all to try.

"Awful good yielders," he says, "and a baby in arms could digest 'em spite of their name — 'Little Satans'."

Jud thrashing beans

"Meat hungry"

THE TOWN FOOL?

NOW Simple Sam hain't alw'ys such a fool as some folks like to make out, and of'times them that hecter him is liable to git 'bout as good as they send. Of course, in most ways he is no'count, and jest manages to live a han'-to-mouth half-fed existence, someway, b'tween what odd jobs he kin pick up, and a little town aid.

Knowin' Sam's fondness for animals, Cap'n Deck let him have a young yoke-a steers one year to care for and earn what he could with 'em workin' out. But Sam couldn't seem to make enough to feed them and him proper, so they had to be took away from him. 'Twuz said round aft'wards that he throwed himself face down in the corner the barn where they'd been tied and wept like a young-un.

He lives alone in the ell of his gramp's ole place, amid trash and clutter, and no furnishin's except a box or two and a cornhusk bedtick on the floor in one corner, 'longside a Magnetic Pearl wood stove which is banked up with floor sweepin's from all sides.

The town allows Sam a barr'l of flour a year, and it's a sight to see him build a batch-a biscuits. He jest dusts some sody and salt right onto the flour in the barr'l, fingers it in, adds pork fat and vinegar an' water to make a dough, tears it up into a pan and shoves it into "Pearl's" smokey innards — for better or wuss.

Sam kep an ole rooster he called "Henry," for comp'ny, two-three years, but bein' dre'ful meat-hungry one spell in the middle the winter, he decided to make stew vittles of him.

Says he, "I put his ole carciss in a kittle o' water, with a rock on the cover to hold his legs down, an' b'iled him all day long. He didn't seem to relax none to speak of, so I cooked him off an' on a'most a week. An' I swear, the cussed critter was so tough then, ye c'd hardly stick a fork in his gravy!"

115

"Simple Sam"

"A pleasant sing"

A SUNDAY EVENING SING

MOST folks seem to enjoy singin' — hymn tunes if they're pious-minded, and pop'lar airs if they ain't. A good sing braces a feller up at times when he's feelin' low in his mind — like the one at John Hall's did last Sund'y after I'd had a broodin' spell. We all enjoyed that evenin' — all but my dog, Pede; he looked like gitt'n a lickin', as usual, and when we begun "Bringin' in the Sheaves," with Jud a-fiddlin', Pede's alto howl swelled the chorus.

One Sund'y evenin' whilst I wuz visitin' with brother Mat in Vermont, we had a pleasant sing at a neighber of his: a pussy little ole maid, Dora sumthin'-or-other. She comp'nied on a new parler organ she'd been breakin' in for a year or more. We sung hymns, mostly, tho a heavy-set nephy of her's (a road runner by occipation, for wimin's dresses and underwear) did wanta sing a comical tune — sumthin' about "down went McGinty to the bottom of the sea," but Dory wouldn't comp'ny him (said 'twould be "sacerreligious"). But he could sing a powerful good bass, and she did let him do "Rocked in the Cradle of the Deep" — jest to please me.

Havin' been disap'inted in love (at fifty), Dory had took up music, for comfort. Fust she got an organ learnin' book, but wuz sixty 'fore she'd saved up enough pennies to git the insterment. They say she learnt ruther slow at fust, pressin' one key to a time and follerin' the notes in the tune book with her left p'intin'-finger. Jaw Jackson, next door to her, wuz tellin' me 'bout it:

"She'd se'down in front of the thing," says he, "and treddle her full of air with both feet, then press one finger on a key and hold it there, b'gorry, till yew wuz sick to yer stomick. By the time she got ready to bear down on another one, her left finger'd slip on the music, or sumthin', and she'd have to begin all over!"

Dora

Shearing

SHEEP

SHEEP ain't raised herebouts as they wuz up to the time I wuz a young-un, tho Father alw'ys kep quite a flock. The perparin' of wool for weavin' into cloth — from the shearin' and washin', to the cardin' and spinnin' — is a home chore that's mostly a thing of the past; when folks perduced a good part of their woolen wear to home. And wimin needed to spin a lot of yarn, them times, with all the stockin's, mittens, mufflers, caps and such they had to knit for their men and young-uns — or a shawl, "fascinater" or "hug-me-tight," for theirselves, and in their day, Mother and Gram also made aplenty cloth and blankets. That ole blue and yaller check lap-robe I use in my pung wuz a blanket they wove on our ole hand loom.

Today, what sheep there is, is mostly out back — tho Jeff Dunkle keeps a few of 'em; some to eat himself and some for the meat cart; disposin' of the fleece to the woolen mill in Neguntic.

A friend of Phil Hall's — Mister "Stuffy" Jenks, painter of livestock by trade — wuz here one year. Awful good at it too. He wuz sketchin' 'longside the sheep parsture one day and Jeff come over to watch him. After a spell Jeff spoke up. "Wisht I could afford to own a sheep paintin' — p'raps, maybe you got one you made a little mistake on, you'd sell me, low?"

So some time after that, Mister Jenks handed him a sketch of a ewe's head, and when he wuz ast the price said, "Oh, anythin' you like." Jeff thot he'd talk it over with his famly, and a doller wuz decided on — but he wanted some horns painted in, to change it from a sheep to a ram.

"Sham, I'd call it!" sputtered Stuffy — and refused to do it.

But Jeff become satisfied and proud (tho considable takenback) when Mister Alden said the sketch might be wuth a hunderd.

"Gorry!" says Jeff.

119

Two young ones

The Picnic

THE HARVEST PICNIC

FARMER folks in town felt like cel'bratin' last fall — it had been such a good season for crops — so they had the bang-up-est harvest picnic I wuz ever to, at the grounds on Clear Pond. Three hayrick loads and a percession of other rigs went from "The Shore." Never see such a crowd nor so much vittles; seems-so evrybody aimed to feed evrybody else. Ole Lisha Jones — well over ninety — wuz there in his stove-pipe hat and flowered vest, as honor'y master-a cerimonies, totterin' round, welcomin' folks.

There wuz a good program of music, and races and games: foot races, swimmin' and p'tater races; bitin' for apples in a tub — a water or hangin' from a string; tryin' to ketch a grease pig, and what not — with considable skylarkin' by young and old.

The band boys set amongst the folks at dinner time and played b'tween bites; and a funny thing happened — one-a them "co-instances." The Brock boys wuz singin' some comical tunes, with part the band for comp'ny, and wuz in the middle of "There wuz a little frog and he lived in a well," when Eb Linden thot sumthin' ailed his baratone horn, tipped her over, and I swear! Out hopped a couple-a leapfrogs. (The work of some dev'lish young-un, probly.)

One frog appeared kind-a sound-dizzy or sumthin' and hopped, tackin' this way and that on a course which landed him in the middle of a custud pie of Aunt Gus'es. Godfrey! Warn't she mad!

Gussie felt so bad over that pie (which nobody would eat), she had one'f her stomick upsets. Took her usual remidy — a teaspoon of gravel — and after a time said she felt easier. (She got that gravel eatin' notion from hens, which, she argues, has the best digestion of any livin' thing, and alw'ys take it with their meals.)

Aside from that, 'twuz an awful nice picnic.

121

"Apple bitin'"

On the fishing grounds

TRAWL FISHING

WHAT good times George, Jab and I did use to have on the trips we made evry fall to Hawk Island, in the ole pinkey, "Flossie Belle," trawl fishin'! We wuz all young and rugged, and in them days fish wuz so plenty in the east bay we only set two-three tub-a trawl, a three-hunderd hook line to each tub, and could soon fill evry barr'l in the hold with fish, salted down.

We gen'ly anchored in Stone Haven and lived ashore in a little buildin' which had a stove and some bunks. George wuz a good cook — with plenty lobsters, clams, and fish to work with — and ole man Drinkwater, who lived nigh, pervided milk and eggs (but with an eye to gittin' a considable taste of our licker). We took comfort.

Jest forty years later, I fished there once agin with two grannephies in The Carrie. Trawlin' warn't what it use to be, but we got enough fish to cure for the winter, for all the famly.

We come home round Mount Desert — never havin' been that way. Stopped over night in Bar Harber, and the boys (bein' young) went ashore, girlin'. Left in the mornin', thotless, with nothin' aboard to eat but a big can-a beans, a few crackers, and a clam chowder, which slid off the ile stove all over the cabin floor, in a little squall. Then the wind died and it come on to rain.

We drifted down the west side the island all day, stayin' our appetites with sody crackers and a few steam clams — savin' the beans for supper. Anchored at nightfall, wet and hungry; lit the stove, drank some hot gingy tea — and opened them beans.

Waal sir! Imagine three famished fishermen, with mouths all perpared for beans, sett'n round wilted like gazin' into a can-a vittles which wuz labeled wrong, containin' (of all things) squash!

Baiting trawl

"Lookin' him in the eye, solemn."

A FUNERAL

AS a rule I don't b'lieve in speakin' no ill of the dead, but of all the cussed, contrary, crabbed ole two-legged bears that ever drew the breath-a life, "Crabby Aaron" wuz the wust. The day his soul and body parted comp'ny, I happ'ned to see Doc Tibbets and ast him what the complaint was that fin'lly finished the ole critter. "Complaint? I hain't heard a single complaint," says Doc (b'hind his hand), "evrybudy seems perfectly satisfied."

Havin' wore out his own famly and bein' old, all alone, and crumpled up with rheumatiz, Aaron, some ten or more years back had arranged with Nanny Twitchel and her pa to have 'em come live at his place and take care of him the rest of his days, agreein' to leave 'em the property when he passed on. Then he perceeded to do evry dev'lish thing he could think of to make it hard as he could for 'em. And what cussedness didn't he think up! If anybudy ever earned a home on this earth, Nanny and her pa did.

Waal, the day of the fun'ral, Will Frisbie appeared with the hearse and a decrepit old hoss, a black sway-back with the heaves.

After the service the percession started over the road for the grave, and things went all right down hill as fur as the bridge. But from there up no'th Trap Hill and the half-mile grade up the back road to the cemetary, that ole hoss wheezed and puffed (fore and aft) stiddy an' regler most evry step of the way — "whee — hic" — ! "whee — hic" — ! "whee — hic" — !

The burial over, elder Brock hunted up Will. Lookin' him in the eye, solemn, he borried a nibble of t'baccy and says, says he, "Willum — the next time I have occasion to 'ficiate at a funeral in these parts, and you supply a conveyance for the departed, I — er — hm — would prefer one that don't go by steam."

125

"Crabby Aaron"

"Hold still"

TAILORING

FOR some years now the stores in Bayport and Neguntic has been sellin' suits ready made, and sister Lucy has made use of what she learnt about tailerin' from Aunt Tildy, by makin' vests to home for a manifact'rer to the west'ard where the stores git their clothin'.

But as a rule store clo'es hain't the comfort you got when an able tailer like ole Button Jones cut a piece-a goods to fit your dimensions; f'rinstance, the long-wearin' and easy-feelin' suits he built from some cloth Gram wove on the ole loom and give me fust time I married. Lor'! Nowadays ye're apt to see a feller in a suit of ready-mades that hang like a gunny sack on a bean-pole! And the pants can't compare with them Button hired Aunt Tildy to make to home for years 'fore he retired from bizness in Bayport.

Kind'f amusin' how the men 'long shore — and some out back — got to comin' to that double an' twisted ole maid to git their pants built, after she got through with Button and went in for herself. Wuz there the fust time she measured a man. Ike Woodford had tore his pants purty bad on a nail at the shop, and took 'em to Tildy to darn. Then he winked at me and dared her to measure him for a new pair. She puckered her mouth a minute, then got out her tape measure and went to it, him a-teasin' her in his aggavatin' way.

"Tildy," says he, "hain't ye a little mite nervous, sleepin' here nights, alone and unpertected, with so many pants round the house?"

"Hush up! you great lummox, and hold still 'fore I stick a pin in you! Now, if you want I should make you a pair-a pants, I'll do it, but if ye're jokin', you kin go to Tophit!"

And that's how she started in for herself; and done so well, she had to hire Lucy for a helper, and fin'lly bought herself a new sewin' machine, the fust one seen or used in these parts.

"Button" Jones

Daniel Webster Gilkey, speaking

POLITICS

THE avrage voter don't seem to take too much in'rest in gov'ment, no matter how much he bellyaches 'bout what he gits in return for the taxes he pays. But like many another poor citizen, I kind-a enjoy goin' to town meetin' to hear them who do like to spill wind, argy and spat over tryin' to organize things.

There's Dan Gilkey; he lives over the Bayport line and has alw'ys been quite a feller for pol'tics. He helped organize "The Blaine Boosters" when Blaine run for President. I 'tended a big rally in the Bayport op'ry house one night; held after a torchlight perade which marched round town and then right into the hall and down the center lane to the stage. The band set 'longside and the torch-lighters stood round the edges the hall (tho they fin'lly had to be ast to put out the torches, they smoked and stunk so).

Noted pol'ticians — and hangers-on — occipied the platform, and lo an' behold if amongst 'em warn't Dan'l Webster Gilkey!

The head chairman started the meetin' by spoutin' hot air till you felt like openin' the winders, then interduced two-three speakers — and then Dan, as a "repisentive of the farmin' class."

'Twuz a mite evident that Dan's courage had been powerf'ly stim'lated. He stepped for'ard, opened his mouth (and hicupped) jest as our congressman slipped in and set down b'hind him (him not realizin' who 'twuz). Evrybudy clapped a lot, and then had to snicker, when Dan — takin' the applause for himself — bowed.

When he could make himself heerd, he begun — "Ladies — an' — feller (hic) cit'zens — thankee! When I think-a m'self havin' the audac'ty t'be — inhabitin' — th'same platform — with all these noted gen'lemen, I — it — I feel (hic) — paralyzed!"

And that's as fur as they let him git.

A "torchlighter"

Repairing Trap bridge

BRIDGES

SUMTHIN' entertainin' about the ways of a crew-a men on town work here — specially roads and bridges: evrybudy takin' a hand at bossin', and hardly a rock, timber, or load-a dirt is handled without a mess of contrary opinions, argyments and whys an' wherefores. But a good part-a the men is liable to be workin' out their taxes, and of'times it's a "lick an' a promise" as fur's results go. Maybe that's why Trap Bridge never did git raised so but a spring freshet or extreme high tide 'll flood her. Up Vermont way, they got sense enough to build their bridges well above flood water and house 'em in aginst the weather. Trap Bridge ought-a be so built.

The ice and water did wreck her bad one spring, takin' out the no'th span, entire. For sevral days there wuz only a foot-bridge over the gap, and supplies goin' across, no'th or south, had to be wheelbarrered or ferried by boat. Terrible nuisance!

'Twuz Deck Gilkey — payed off from a trip on a vessel, at that time — who told of cel'bratin' in Bayport, havin' to walk most the way home (over-loaded), and undertakin' to cross the foot bridge.

"Heerd a splash," says he, "an' b'gorry, 'twuz m'self!"

'Twuz him also who wuz ashore in New York when the Brook-lyn Bridge wuz dedicated, and wuz describin' the wonder of it to us at the post office, fiext time he come east. Ole Sam Colbert lis'ned and squinted out the corner of his eye, sceptic'l (the way he does 'bout things he ain't seen himself; him never havin' been more'n twenty miles from Beachmont in his life).

"Quite a bridge, is it, Decky?" says he, raisin' one eyebrow and spittin', contempt'us like. "Waal, I bet ye if I could-a crossed her with that hefty yoke-a steers of mine, Star an' Bright, in their prime, with a load of green cordwood — she'd-a creaked some!"

A covered bridge

"Rev. Flint" asks a blessing

THE SUNDAY DINNER

I'D never thot'f it till I heerd Doc Tibbets say that folks gen'ly eat the most the day they do the least — Sund'ys. Still, a good stomick-stretchin' dinner has alw'ys been a form of dissipation even the most righteous 'lowed their flesh to indulge in after a mornin' in church havin' their souls put in order.

My father wuz a good pervider, and Mother wuz a famous cook, and she gen'ly spent the best part of Sat'd'y perparin' vittles for the "day o' rest," and took pride in loadin' up the ole table to full capacity — specially if anybody wuz invited in to set with us.

But no matter how eager folks was to pitch in, we all had to bow and wait through Father's modritely spoken blessin'; us boys a-fidgetin' (and I'm afeared with noses more occipied, sniffin' the good smells, than our ears, a-lis'nin' to the holy words). But, when the parson and famly wuz ast to Sund'y dinner, he wuz apt to have wind enough left — after a len'thy mornin' sermon — to give us and the vittles a blessin' that was a blessin' (same's the ole-fashion Rev. Flint does today). Warn't it Ben Franklin who sujjested blessin' all the vittles in the bulk — in in the cellar, shed, or buttry — to save time at the table? Awful good idee, anyway.

Even aboard a vessel cook gen'ly made up sumthin' sweet for Sund'y to top off the usual salt junk, 'taters and yaller biscuits; raisin puddin' as a rule, and if "The Ole Man" (Cap'n) wuz feelin' good, we might git a noggin of sperits for a starter.

Waal, I s'pose if yer gizzard's in good workin' order of a Sund'y, there's a cert'n amount of hog comfort in stuffin' yer body with sevral plates full of good-tastin' fodder; then lazin' round, stupid like, while Nature sorts it over for what good she kin git out'f it (with the aid of a little bakin' sody, maybe).

133

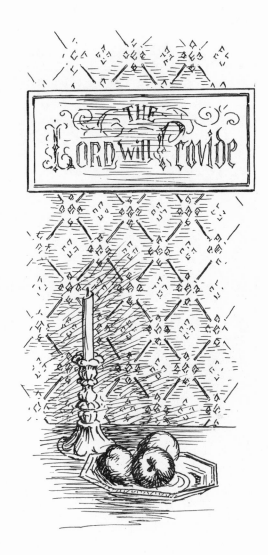

Faith

Gene, at work

COOPERING

EVER since they put stave an' head machinry into the mill and built the fust cooper shop 'longside, Gene's been makin' lime casks for the kiln. But of late years there's been orders for so many lime, apple, and p'tater barr'ls to ship away that he's had to larn cooperin' to some the young fellers. It makes quite a little industry now, b'tween the mill work and five-six cooper shops goin'. And quite a few of us outside earn a doller at odd times cuttin' birch and alder poles and splittin' and shavin' 'em for hoops. Many's the winter evenin' I've spent a-straddle a shavin' hoss.

Gene, a withy, touch-tempered man with rusty gray hair that use to be fire-red, says he's been "wras'lin' barr'ls" for forty years, and his legs has growed crooked from usin' 'em, one way and another, most as much as he does his arms, in puttin' a cask together. But he's still quick's a cat, and he proved it, jest lately.

That smart tub-a guts, Sumner Creal, breezed into the shop 'bout a week ago, and handed Gene a trick cigar. After it exploded under his nose, he rushed Sumner and they started scufflin' — Sumner larfin' and tauntin'. But how he did change his tune when Gene jumped aboard of him and locked them barr'l-grippin' legs round him amidships, a trick he'd learnt from wras'lers at the county fair — "scissers hold," he says they calls it.

Waal sir! He had the big lubber face down in a heap-a-shavin's, gaspin', groanin', and all done; then got his boy to help him fit a couple-a hoops round Sumner's gut line, tight, with the locks behind. And Sumner (chop-fallen, for once), weak, and gruntin', and barely able to git onto his feet and into his buggy, had to drive off, lookin', as you might say, like a human hogshead.

Served him right.

135

The "human hogshead"

Fortune telling

GYPSIES

IF you want-a see sparks fly, jest mention the word "gypsy" to Jim — and this is the why of it. On one the days he wuz goin' out back peddlin' with his dry goods an' notions cart, he circled out by way of the Bayport road. Seein' a band of gypsies comin' to'ard him, he whipped up his hoss to git by 'em on the run, but had to slow down when they wouldn't budge from takin' up the whole road. And when he got amongst 'em, they swarmed aboard of him, pertendin' to buy. But while three-four haggled over a few pennies wuth of stuff, the rest helped theirselves aplenty b'hind his back, as he found out later when he took 'count of stock. Warn't he mad?

I wouldn't say they're all like that, but, as Gram Dunkle says, "the on'y time y'ever need lock house or barn is when the gypsies come to town." Then she'll tell of cases she's "heern of" where the critters lugged off "back-loads" from folks's wood piles or gardens after dark — or even "wras'led" a quart or two of milk from a stray cow for their babies "in broad daylight."

But whether or no; it's a funny way to live, roamin' and squattin' all over the country. They're entertainin' critters, in a way, and some is purty able at music. You don't see the menfolks hurtin' theirselves with work none, but they look well fed enough. Must git their money tradin'; shrewd hoss traders, I understand.

The wimin folks perfess to tell fortunes, and the town gals think it a lark to have their hands read. While I wuz workin' with a crew-a men on the underpinnin' to Trap Bridge, a parcel of gypsy wenches bore down on us wantin' to tell our fortunes, and held up opprations half an hour. Persistent critters! (And I'd say, the village gals could larn p'ints on stirrin' a man's blood from the dark-eyed young petticoat that read my calluses!)

Gypsy fiddler

Getting out ice

ICE

YES, we fishermen do have to have quite a little ice to keep our shippin' fish chilled — specially durin' the salmon season — but gen'ly git aplenty, good enough, right here in the Frog Pond. The best grade ice for home and hotel use comes from Clear Pond, which is spring fed, and where you kin see bottom in thutty foot of water on a calm day in the open seasons. Walt Farrer owns the cuttin' rights there, and durin' the winter soon's she's friz thick enough, him and his crew-a men yank out and store tons of it.

How do they go 'bout it? Waal, the ice is fust cleared of snow, if there's any, and a sizeable hole cut. Then, with a board for a straightedge, they start from the hole and saw a long strip 'bout fourteen inches wide, crack it loose and saw it into cakes as it's floated into the hole endways. By doin' the same with another strip at right angles to the fust strip, it opens up water on two sides of a square to work from — if that's clear to you. In real cold weather the cakes is left afloat till a team is ready to take a load to the icehouse — else they might freeze together or down to where they set.

Walt peddles quite a lot of it — mostly to summer folks. One city schoolmarm has a kind of ice bucket with a can inside, which turns with a crank, for churnin' diffrent flavers of friz cream. She took a mess of the fust she made over the road to ole Cousin Enos (who'd never saw none b'fore). He sniffed it, took out his chaw and spooned a sizeable chunk of the cold stuff into his mouth.

She says he shivered, balanced it on his tongue with his mouth open a minute, then chawmped it once and gulped it down. Then, soon's he could git his breath, he opened his eyes, handed back the dish, and put his chaw back — to limber up his tongue.

"Dum cold fodder, Miss Perkins!" he wheezed.

139

Uncle Enos

Chen Dacey

THE PRINTER

FOLKS seem to find the "Bayport Bugle" ent'tainin'? Waal, the editor, Chen Dacey, does aim to make it live up to the motter printed at the top of the front page: "Bright — Newsy — Independent — Saucy." Anyway, he's an ent'tainin' critter himself, and alw'ys busier'n the devil at a church picnic, what with gittin' out the weekly paper — written and set up mostly by himself — and doin' job printin'.

Chen's an old bach, and you'll find him at the Bugle office all times of day or night. Bunks in a back room and eats at his desk, mostly on doughnuts and coffee. But he's smart! Writes the news in an in'restin' way, also pomes and stories, and a card he gives out to bizness folks says, "You greet your custermers with a smile — why not let your ad. do the same?" So when he makes up an advertisement, they're alw'ys gay or comical. And when he wants some odd or fancy letters, a face, figger, or orniment to suit his own idees, he'll whittle out "woodcuts" himself. Clever critter!

Chen tought school a year or two when he fust come to Bayport, and at odd times got to helpin' George Rusten, who then owned and edited The Bugle. And when George died, Chen took it over. Then, aimin' to put more life into the paper, he invented the motter.

But durin' one state 'lection campaign, The Bugle got a mite too sassy, and a puffed-up feller townsman, who wuz runnin' for some office, brought suit for libel, had Chen arrested and he wuz clapped into the lock-up over a night 'fore he got bailed out. But he writ a trick pome of apoligy there, to put in the paper, which wuz so comical and meechin', the feller dropped the case.

Later on the trick in the pome wuz found out. If you read the fust letters in all the lines, down'ards, it went like this:

Y
O
U
B
T
E
L
L
I
E
D
H
Y
P
O
C
R
I
T
I
C
A
L
W
N
D
B
A
G

An "advertizement"

At the Springport Fair

COUNTRY FAIRS

MY sister Lucy bought some flower bulbs at the Bayport Fair last year from a fereign lookin' peddler, three for fifty cents. His sample plants wuz full of big, purty blossoms, she said, but them bulbs turned out to be some kind of an onion, or sumthin' like. So, she went agin this year figgrin' if he wuz there agin, she'd demand her money back and give him a talkin' to. But he warn't there. Too many cheats work country fairs. Up to Bangor one fall, a shell-game feller took two silver dollers from me.

There wuz good exhibits of evrythin' at the town fair last year, includin' a fat-baby show in addition to the usual livestock. The half-mile hoss race down the road didn't amount to much, but the ox pullin' wuz real excitin'; and a tug-o'-war b'tween The Trap and The Center wuz won by the Trap men without hardly a grunt. Farmers may be good at pushin', but sea-farin' men know how to pull.

On Labor Day an excursion wuz organized to go up river to the Springfort Fair in that little ole steamer, Water Lily.

One-a the main attractions at the fair groun's (for the men folks at least) wuz some Haywayan dancin' girls in straw petticoats who contortioned in a tent on a high stage. I found the place packed, and our ole cap'n right up front, jest as close as he could git. Ev'dently the gals done their dressin' un'neath the platform and what'd Ole Cap do but git out his knife, pry a knot loose, wink at the crowd, and have himself a private peek. But purty soon, a swarthy wench in a wrapper appeared above his head (and the words she hove at him warn't nothin' she'd learnt as fur from Americy as no South Seas, I'd say). How the crowd did howl!

After the show, Cap'n confided to me that the peek wuz wuth a scoldin'. "Awful purty-sparred critters!" says he.

Old fool!

The cheat

"Nigh swallered my pipe-stem"

THE BATHING BEACH

QUITE a few folks from Bostin and other cities do their summer vacationin' at Beachmont of late years. Some is a mite high-uppity with us "natives," but the majority is sociable enough. It brings us in a little extry bizness and some new faces to look at for a few weeks anyway—which is probly a good thing.

Most evry fair day a cert'n number of the summer boarders is on the beach, lazin' round in the sun, tannin' (or burnin') their hides, or pertendin' they enjoy goin' into the water. Some-a the men swim, more or less, but the wimin jest splash round and squeal — and they do wear the consarndest lookin' rigs! Godfrey!

One warm mornin', early, I see that thin Alabamy cullud feller (drives for a tony family at the hotel) come gallopin' down the steep side the beach and up to his middle in the cold water, 'fore losin' headway. He friz rigid, shoulders hunched. They say he's a pious feller and never swears, but soon's he got his breath he rolled his eyes to heaven and chattered, "Chee-ee-sus — and crackers!" stiff-legged it for home, put on his overcoat and went back to bed.

Another aft'noon John Colbert, from Six Corners, set above the beach a-watchin' out-a curos'ty. He wuz tellin' me 'bout it. "Wind nor'west for two days," says he, "and it made me shudder to see some-a them folkses step into that water. One woman in regler clo'es peeled off her shoes and stockin's behind an umbrella and waded in with her skirts furled up round her middle! I swow!

"There wuz some purty scandlous skylarkin' goin' on too, it seemed to me. One sassy hairpin hove me a kiss when she went by — and I nigh swallered my pipe stem. Told my woman 'bout it when I got home, and she 'lowed I probly encouraged the hussey.

"Wimin is funny," says John.

"Up to his middle"

Milt's shop

THE TINKER

WHEN it comes to makin' or mendin' most anythin' under heavens, Milt Kester is a jeenous. He started out to be a farmer after takin' over his brothers' in'rests in the old place, but his mechanical cant interferred more'n more as time went on: boat buildin', millin', and all kinds of tinkerin' jobs folks brung him. So today his fields is all growin' up to brush, and the only farmin' done on the place is a kitchen garden and a few hens.

But after all seems-so a man ought-a foller his natural bent, if he can, and Milt kin mend, or manifacture most anythin' from a clo'espin to a sailin' craft or wagin.

Six year ago he shifted his shop from the barn at home to the buildin' back of Mason Hall in Beach Village where he is now, busy at a thousand diffrent jobs. The fust thing he done, soon's he moved in, wuz to finish and set up some foot power machinry he'd started to build; for light sawin', jig-sawin', grindin', turnin' and so on. And now he kin make as neat and purty a piece of furniture as you kin buy to the west'ard.

The only time I ever knew Milt to show a serious lack of sense wuz when he got messed up with inventin' a perpetchul motion engine. He spent hours and days on it gittin' it together, and to'ard the last his woman said he got crotchety and couldn't sleep, and stayed home, workin' day and night on the cussed contraption. And when 'twuz done 'twouldn' go, even if you give it a push. Fin'lly, Milt bellered a string-a cusses, hove it into the woodshed, and got the fust good night's sleep he'd had in a fortnight.

The next day he wuz himself agin, busy at his shop and singin' while he worked, as usual:

"Hr-mp die iddle die iddle dee doo — r-rmp die iddle dee doo!"

"Perpetchul motion"

The church balcony

OLD CENTER CHURCH

SHE'S old beyond my memry, but Center folks alw'ys did and still do support a preacher for it. Father, bein' as conscientious as he was pious, use to drive us all out there to meetin' them Sund'ys when there warn't none at the Shore church. And Heaven knows I've weathered through some awful len'thy sermons in the house-a God (mostly asleep). But 'twarn't only young-uns who dozed off; many's the time I've seen some nappin' ole deacon come to with a snort when his woman planted an elbow in his ribs.

I figger young-uns, like dogs, is naturally good jedges of men; so some parsons I liked, and some I didn't. The one who had the old church longest (when I wuz young and obliged to go), and who, in a way, swung me off the "straight an' narrer," wuz the Revrend Dribbley, one-a them weepy sky pilots. Now it may be good ministrin' to git your flock all worked up to sheddin' tears over whether their souls is bound for the right port or not; but from the day he wept over my shoulder, I wuz inclined to be a black sheep.

Of the parsons we've had late years, one I liked use to visit "in'restin' sinners" and smoke a pipe, with no talk of religion. But he warn't pop'lar with the ole hard-shells and didn't last long. Another good feller wuz "Docter" Katson, an Englishman, who reminded you a good deal of Abe Lincoln. And I callate he wuz likewise too much like ordnary mortals, for he didn't last long either. Maybe his way of pernouncin' warn't liked, his "els," perticly.

After prayer meetin' one Frid'y evenin', the leadin' brethren discussed the need of a vestry for the Sund'y School and Docter Katson sujjested buildin' a "hell" onto the rear of the church.

Staunch old buildin'. Wuth visitin'. You kin still see my name jack-knifed into one-a the stalls in the south side balcony.

"The Rev. Dribbley"

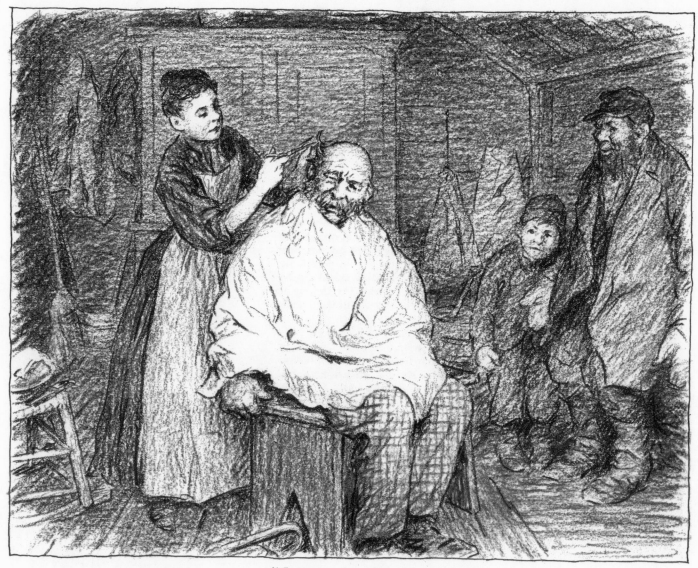

"Jessie, barberin'"

BARBERING

'TWOULD be a blessin' if someone could think up a hair-cuttin' tool you could use on yerself as easy's shavin'. Tom Kester did forge a pair of shear handles bent-ways so he could do quite a job on himself with two-three lookin' glasses, but most'f us gen'ly git our hair sheared by one-a the famly or a neighber — 'nless we're goin' to town an'll pay fifteen cents to git it done.

Milt Kester is a good hair barber, and learnt his daughter, Jessie, to do his for him. She got so clever at it all the menfolks in the famly, and most the neighbers, got to askin' her to do theirn. A comidatin', purty little critter, but with a tongue in her head. Nobudy paid her nothin', or much, so she wuz sassy as your please, with a trick of usin' yer ears to twist yer head by, and a cuff side the head if you didn't keep yer hands to yerself.

I callate Will Tubman in his day done more barbrin' ('long with tooth yankin') than anybody in town, b'fore or since. They even say there's hair from most'f his feller townfolks mixed into the plastrin' of the "oppratin' room" he added to the store. Will's youngest boy, "Mitty," took up barbrin' for an occipation and still works in Jason Doherty's shop in Bayport. Stepped in to see him last time I wuz in town and there wuz four-five old-timers, aidin' and abettin' Dan Gilkey in a perfane rendrin' of the tune about Paddy and the barber; Mitty playin' a mouth organ, Jason wavin' time with a shavin' brush, and a fat feller in the barber's chair blowin' a hole through a mess-a lather to jine in.

"Yore go'dam ole razor is not wuth a drot,

An' wouldn't cut butter unless 'twuz made hot!" they wuz a-bellerin', as I come in, and I helped swell the chorus.

"For to lather an' shave, to lather an' shave,

To lather an' shave an' frizzle my chin!"

151

"To lather an' shave"

"Overboard he went"

ICE BOATING

THE only iceboat I ever see wuz the one Al Cobe built to home one fall, in sections, from a plan he took out-a his farm paper. I helped him team her up to Camp Porky on Long Pond where we put her together, and soon's there wuz ice thick enough he larnched her and tried her out. She wuz the dev'ls own tetchy craft to handle, but after he got the hang of "solid-water sailin'," him and the boys had a lot-a fun with her for sevral winters.

There wuz a cold spell follerin' the Janooary thaw that fust winter and the pond was glib as glass. Jab Tubman (the nosey ole sea-dog) had been cur'ous about the iceboat, so Al thot 'twould be a good time to take him over for a sail. When they clim aboard Jab wuz for takin' the tiller, but Al sujjested that he be jest a pass'nger the fust "voyage," and to hang on, "teeth and toenails!"

They started over the ice with a fresh, fair breeze-a wind, and were soon goin' faster'n Jab had ever moved in all his life. Nigh the upper end the pond he le'go one hand to tighten his hat jest as Al was comin' about, and quicker'n scat, overboard he went, and slid most a couple-a hunderd feet on his shoulder blades 'fore he fetched up in a smother-a snow mongst some bushes ashore.

Al made round and dropped sail so's to git him aboard agin — but "no more iceboatin' " for Jab. He unsnarled himself, grad- ual, sputterin' "dammits!"; pulled an alder branch down out-a one sleeve and got onto his feet, limp-kneed and shakey.

Ignorin' Al, he ventured out onto the ice lookin' for his hat, short steppin', teeterin' and slippin' aginst the wind.

Ashore agin, he still ignored Al and plowed up through the brush and crusted snow to'ard the road home (madder'n a hornet)!

"Invention of the dev'l!" Al heerd him snort.

153

Al Cobe

"Laizin' 'round"

LAZY BONES

MOST seasons there's aplenty blueb'ries in the parstures by the back roads, for them that cares to pick 'em. 'Bout as soon pick fleas out'f a bearskin myself, but some folks seem to make quite a picnic out-a the back-achin' job of gathrin 'em for home use, or for the stage to take to town and dispose of for 'em.

There's Lazy, f'rinstance (his name's Lazerous, but the nickname fits him most the time). He's the pickin'est critter I ever did know. Sort-a hibernates durin' the cold weather and ain't really up an' round much till there's sumthin' to pick. And when the berries begin to ripen, he starts pickin' near and far, till they're done: blueb'ries, rawsb'ries, blackb'ries, cranb'ries; and even wuthless culch like pucker berries. He said to me once, "Some likes to fish, and some likes to hunt," ("and some likes to work," thinks I) "but I like to go pickin'," says he. It is the nighest thing to work he shows any gumption at. It might be fruit today and tomorrer "nanny plums," which he gathers in Jeff's sheep parsture and sells to a flower farmer in Neguntic for fertilizer.

But he kin pick a chicken quicker'n anyone I know. Makes a few cents pickin' fir balsom spills, trailin' pine and ferns, but most the year he jest lazies round with a houn' dog who's equally lazy. To keep the wolf from the door, when there ain't nothin' to pick, his woman Lizzie knits nets or works out at anythin' she kin git.

Speakin' of the dog — while follerin' Lazy cranb'ryin' one day, the fool critter stepped into a ground hornet's nest, but after one lis'less leap, he jest laid down, closed his eyes, and whimpered and yowled while they stung him — ruther than hurry off fast enough to git rid of 'em. They say Lizzie had to feed him spoon vittles for a week, his muzzle wuz swole up so.

155

"Lazy"

The medicine lecture

MEDICINE

SUMTHIN' or other ails most evrybudy at one time or another, if not all the time, seems-so. Still, I dunno's this village would be a perticler good stand for a docter. Most of us seem to perfer to choose our own medicine. Of course, now and agin we do have to git Doc Tibbets or Adams to come over from Bayport or Neguntic for such mergincies as jinin' up a busted bone or helpin' fetch a young-un into the world, or to grab you from the brink-a the grave, when all else fails. But mostly we git along with what medicines they sell at the store, or the mail-stage kin git for us, or which we send for to the manifact'rers of remidies who advertise in the farm papers or the Bayport Bugle.

'Bout once a year a travlin' docter comes through here, sellin' Indian remidies, and some who has tried 'em won't use no others. Gen'ly gits a young-un to go round town with handbills, and then sets up a stand by the post office for letcherin' and sellin'. He had an old Indian with him last time, and set him on a soap box — most naked — for ex'bition. ('Bout as nigh's he ever got to soap, I jedged, by his looks.) But, spite-a that, the docter said the old "chief" had reached the age of a hunderd an' ten years by takin' a "lixir" made by the medicine man of his tribe, and his lixir and all the remidies on sale "come from Nature's own garden."

Ole Sam Colbert tried out some-a the salve for a "fever-sore" on his shin and swore it worked wonders. Sam makes a terrable touse when anythin' ails him. "Angriest, angriest thing I ever suffered with!" says he, shettin' his eyes and groanin' through his nose at the thots of it. "Got so bad one spell, I had to set on the aidge of my drinkin' water spring and hang my shank down in the cole water to chill the grief out'f it! Angry? Angry!"

"Store" medicine

Harvesting potatoes

POTATOES

To me a meal-a vittles ain't complete without p'taters, and I figger there must be more of 'em et than any other one article of human fodder — exceptin' bread, maybe. Anyway, it's the biggest crop in this state, and a powerful sight of 'em is shipped out.

The farmers herebouts raise good uns, but p'taters do better out back, where there ain't so much fog. Al Small, back of Sharp Hill, perduces the best quality, and takes a lot-a pains to make 'em so. He'll go down the rows evry day or so with some kerosene in a can, knockin' the p'taters bugs off the vines into it with a stick. Comes to the shore evry fall for sevral cart loads of rockweed; lets it rot over the winter and uses it for dressin', with a little phosphate. It makes an awful nice p'tater, smooth, and good flaver; and he gits a fancy price for 'em for seed.

You don't see p'tater balls growin' on the vines so much, late years, for some reason. It's the fruit of the plant you know —sumthin' like a little termater. Mother use to make pickles of 'em.

Yaas sir, the homely spud is a right useful eatin' article.

I well rec'lect my good mother on a cold winter's mornin' b'fore I started off for school, puttin' a hot baked p'tater and a b'iled egg in each my side coat pockets, for my dinner, and to keep my hands warm walkin' the two miles to the schoolhouse.

Meat an' p'taters, fish an' p'taters, salt pork an' p'taters; p'taters b'iled, baked, fried — anyway you like 'em — is my idee of the right foundation for a meal-a vittles.

Some folks is satisfied to se'down, two-three times a day, to sody biscuits, sass, sweet culch, and tea; or, fill their belly full of riz-bread — poor stuff for an outdoor man's gizzard to grind on. I 'bout's soon go out into a fog storm and garp an' swaller.

159

Gathering seaweed

The carriage shop

THE CARRIAGE BUILDER

WHAT we called "the ole gristmill" wuz also the fust saw-mill, with an up-an'-down saw at the no'th end. And ole "up-t'day-an'-down-t'morrer" wheezed its way through all the logs that come down Trap Stream up to the time the Dassets built the new mill t'other end of the dam and fitted her out with circler saws.

Some five years before the ole mill burnt, Lycander Burkett took over the power end of it for a wheelwright and wagin repair shop and added a band saw and lathe to the machinry. "Sanny" had come from down state, and 'twuz much as a year 'fore we found out he wuz a fust-class carriage builder and fancy painter. 'Twuz the year after Andrew Muzzey started peddlin'. He needed a regler tin-peddler's cart, so him and Sanny put their heads together over the plans and Sanny took the job. And after some weeks when Andrew come back from a trip, he wuz showed as purty a piece of cabinetwork on wheels as you ever see — all painted, striped, and lettered.

Ole man Frisbie wuz so taken with the job he ordered Sanny to build him a spring top sleigh, and 'twuz a beauty when finished.

After the fire Sanny moved to Bayport and pardnered with Joe Bacon in a shop, handlin' mostly fancy carriage work. He's still there, and only recent done an odd job for the town band. The band needed a new bass drum, but hadn't the sev'nty-five dollers.

"Build you one for twenty-five," says Sanny, "carriage work bein' slack, and if it don't please you, don't take it."

All hands agreed, so he sent away for the calfskin heads, but done all the rest himself; from caliprin' down the thin birch for the sides, to the makin' and puttin' together of evry last part of it, and then finishin' her with stain, varnish, gole leaf, and lettrin', as good a drum as you'd buy out'f a catalogue.

161

"Sanny"

Mending nets

A NET FISHERMAN

QUITE a few groundfish: haddock, cod and hake, come into the bay, spring and fall; tho Pete didn't git too many with his nets this last fall 'count of there bein' so many dogfish. There hain't many that I know of in the bay that uses nets for bottom fishin', most'f us perferrin' to trawl or handline. Pete's been fishin' here now four-five seasons stiddy. Kind'f a cur'ous feller, but pleasant and comidatin'. Come from Provincetown way eriginally, they say. Portigee. Lives aboard his sloop all the year round; hauled out over in Bayport durin' the winter and moored here in the Cove the rest the year. Jest him and his dog. "Fish houn'," is what the boys call the critter. Ain't fed much else I guess.

"Dat w'y heem have so plenty mooch brain," says Pete.

From spring till fall, when he ain't out on the water, you'll gen'ly find Pete down to the ole Farrer fish house, which he uses, potterin' round; dressin' and splittin' fish to salt down and dry, maybe; mendin' his nets, or jest smokin' and meditatin'. Alw'ys is glad to see you. Has a comical way of expressin' himself, and that's probly why city fellers sometimes enjoy hirin' him for a sailin' or fishin' party (spite of the mess he keeps his boat in).

A parcel of artist fellers got Pete to take 'em out to the Pink Islands paintin' one day. I su'mise they had sumthin' b'sides ile and turp'ntine along, and give Pete enough to loosen up his tongue in good shape. He yarned and sung sea chanties all the way home, they said. One chanty, Phil swears, lasted from Pink Island light to Hogback Ledge, seven miles.

Two of the boys has done paintin's of Pete; one with water paints and t'other with iles. The ile paintin', someway, looks the most natural to me (Pete bein' kind-a iley complected).

163

Pete

Mowing by hand

HAYING

Old hay press

DOWN East here fog is kind'f a nuisance, and some summers there's liable to be so much of it 'long shore that farmer folks who winter much livestock ain't alw'ys cert'n of gittin' what hay they need made at the right time and stowed away dry in the barn.

Back of the hills conditions is better. Of'times when it's a thick-a-fog here, the sun'll be shinin' out there. So some the back town farmers specialize in growin' hay to sell, and Carl Hagget runs a hay press, bailin' up considable to ship out. Abner Small has about the best grass farm in town, tho he still mows by hand. What him and his six boys can't cut, he sells standin'. Last winter he didn't have enough hay to carry his stock through, 'count of gittin' two new cows, so he had to buy a few bales.

While they wuz histin' it onto the mow, the tackle stuck. Abner fretted and hopped round (the way he does, impatient, nervous critter), then spit on his hands and clim the rope, hand over hand, to the block under the ridge; most forty foot up. He fussed and yanked a minute, and then, hangin' onto a cross timber by one hand, durned if he didn't unhook the whole block and tackle and drop it, yellin', "See'f you boys kin fix it!" — not stoppin' to think how they wuz gonna git it back to him.

Waal, the fust thing they done wuz to heap up some hay underneath where he hung — him a-gaspin', "Hurry up!" — his legs danglin' and reachin' this way and that.

Their longest ladder wuz thutty foot, but by usin' a pole they managed to reach a rope to him. But he wuz so weak after he got it made fast (with one hand), he slid down 'bout as sudden as fallin', and the rope bein' ten foot too short, he landed backsides fust in the hay and cracked his new teeth.

165

"A tetchin' sight"

THANKSGIVING

JOSH INGALS is a pious man, and a good man, and deserves to prosper. And he has done well ever since he put his fust sav-in's into buyin' the ole Talbert farm, back of Bare Mountin, and worked like a beaver to improve it. Wuz holed up there alone nigh two years, livin' mostly on "mush 'n' m'lasses," he said, till he felt he had the place fixed fit for a wife — and married Mary Gilkey.

He's one the best farmers in town, and forever sperimentin' at raisin' new things. Has done special well with strawb'ries, and last year tried raisin' a few turkeys. I'd never tasted turkey meat, so wuz glad when he ast me out to dinner Thanksgivin' Day.

"Waal, hello, you ole pirate!" says he, when my hoss, "Boa's'n," towed me aboard my box buggy into his dooryard. "How's yer body?"

The weather wuz still and mild, so him and me and his oldest boy pottered round outdoor till we wuz called in to dinner. Josh gen'ly asks a blessin' at the table, but that day he says, "Le's step outdoor a minute." So we all went out the side door — where you git such a nice view of most all his farm — and he gathered his famly round him and ast a blessin' and give thanks right there. Kind'f a tetchin' sight for an ole sinner like me.

He has aplenty to be thankful for: a fertile farm, comf'table home, a rugged, capable woman, and fine boys and girls.

I thot the side dooryard looked considable cluttered up with garden truck, for a man as orderly as Josh, but when I hitched up to go home, he ast me if I'd deliver the stuff for him at the Cove.

"Cert'nly," says I, "where to?"

"To the little house where your gizzard's been grindin' away for so many years, endeavorin' to digest your own cookin'," says he.

A good, gen'rous man, Josh.

Garden truck

"O.C." "cuttin' quirms"

SKATING

I CALLATE they hain't no cozier place to skate in the world than our mill pond, sheltered as it is to the no'thard by Bare Mountin, east and west by woodland and cliff, the dam facin' to the s'uth'ard. And if anybudy should feel chilly, the boys gen'ly has a fire goin' in the cave under the cliff. And so it's been for genrations of young-uns, and youngish old uns, who enjoy skatin'.

We didn't have much snow durin' last Feb'rary and the ice wuz smooth and good. Went up to watch 'em skate a few times. Fust time I went quite a crowd wuz there — and bless my eyes! If amongst 'em warn't that dried up little ole critter "O. C." Small, aboard his ring-nose skates, a-singin', "I don't care a cuss fer no-bud-ee who don't care a cuss for me-ee!" You alw'ys could count on "O. C." gittin' to any place there wuz good skatin' as fur back as I kin remember. Still spry as a weasel and he cert'nly can cut quirms and fancy figgers when he gits loosened up. He dammed up the brook back of his barn a-purpose to have a place to practice on.

The school teacher skated up to me, last day I was at the pond, and told of my youngest grannephy comin' to school the day before, soakin' wet and hangin' with icicles. (The wettin'est young-un!) He'd went to school that mornin' — 'twuz b'low zero — by way of the mill pond, and skated down the west bank on some hard snow crust straddlin' a stick, took a spill, and fetched up in a spring hole.

He didn't dare go home, so Miss Peevey stood him up behind the school stove; and there he stayed, all mornin' long, steamin' and drippin'. Ketched a chill goin' home, his ma told me later; so she put him to bed — after rubbin' his chest with goose grease (and warmin' his bottom). But when he fust took his clo'es off, she said he looked for all the world as if he'd been parb'iled.

169

"Steamin' and drippin'"

Dave's shoeshop

THE SHOE-MAKER

SOME of us ole fellers wuz settin' round in Dave Wallace's shoe shop t'other day and got to discussin' life and the things you go through, for what you git out'f it (or don't git).

Take Dave's life, f'rinstance: born in Vermont, learnt the shoe-maker's trade in his 'teens, went into the war under age and wuz wounded twice. Took a hotel job in Bostin on the way home, had his head turned by a sassy little waiter girl, and married her. She turned out to be a bad-un (drink and drugs), but a boy wuz born to 'em. Then Dave took hotel jobs, here, there, and ev'rywhere. (Wife's actin'-up kep him movin', so I learnt.) His boy died.

Then a friend backed Dave to run a place in Providence. There ten years. The wife fin'lly p'isoned herself. But she musta had some good p'ints, for Dave alw'ys speaks respec'ful of her.

After that he left evrythin' and had drifted down this way, headin' for Bangor by train and stage when he took a notion to stop a spell at the tavern here. Wuz persuaded to take over the managin' of it, and did (till he run afoul the state probition law for sellin' a little licker on the quiet, and quit in disgust).

So, it 'curred to Dave that he might go back to the trade he learnt as a boy. And here he is, gittin' a pension, more contented than he's ever been —so he says. Does repairin' mostly, but kin make a long-wearin' pair-a boots for man, woman or child.

A pleasant-dispositioned man; likes to discuss while he's at work (tho the only chance the rest'f us has to git a word in edge-ways, as a rule, is when he has a mouthful of shoe pegs).

"Life's been kind-a in'restin', after all, hain't it, yew ole sea dogs?" says Dave, "even if most'f us is of about as much impor-tance in the world — as a bug on a bear's bum!"

Dave, in his prime

The red ear

THE HUSKING BEE

THREE-FOUR city fellers (artists) wuz vistin' Phil Hall at his cottage to do some fall paintin', and he entatained 'em some by takin' 'em round to any good times that wuz goin' on. We all went to a corn huskin' at Jed Farrer's one evenin'. Quite a crowd wuz there, as there gen'ly is, for Jed alw'ys pervides a good time; plenty vittles and drink, and a barn dance and songs and games aft'wards. He had a powerful heap of corn in the middle the barn floor, but the folks went right at it and husked it in jig time.

I'd told the fellers b'forehand that any gal caught huskin' a red ear-a corn could be kissed, and sujjested stainin' a few ears with beet juice to plant amongst the heap. So they fixed up some (but with their water colors stead of beet juice), and tucked 'em in on the sly, aimin' to set nigh the purtiest gals.

As luck would have it, Aunt Gussie Colbert husked the fust red ear. She wuz settin' back to the door, and ole Zeke Alby had jest come in with his umbrella, callatin' it looked like rain. Then he spotted the red ear in Gussie's hand and smacked her good.

"Marcy sakes! Zeke Alby! Y'had fried mack'rel for supper!"

We poke fun at Zeke's umbrella, the biggest one I ever did see. He says a regler one don't cover him fore an' aft (he bein' bent over so from a fall he got aboard a vessel years ago). So when he's under way in a rain storm, all you kin see from b'hind is the ole bumblesheet and a pair of brogans crumplin' along. I ast him once what he'd do if a squall caught him with it up.

"Do?" says he. "What any sailer man would do! — luff'er, an' spill the wind out'f'er!"

The boys all seemed to enjoy the huskin' party, and thot it a mighty pleasant way to git a job done.

Zeke Alby

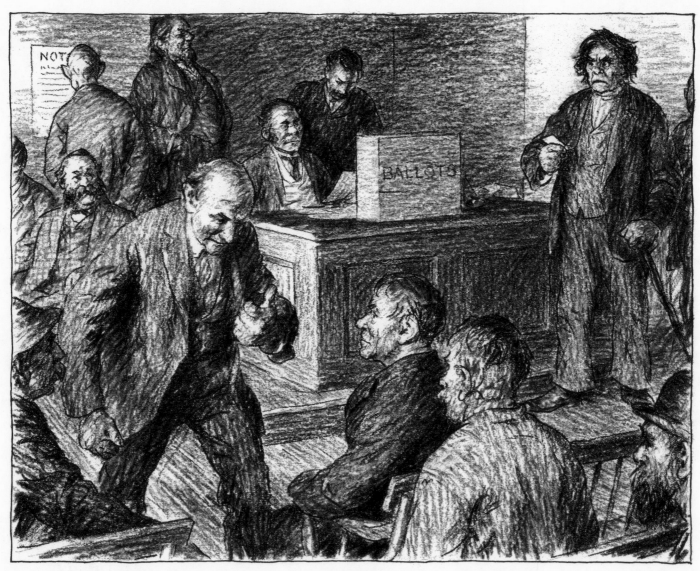

Voting

TOWN MEETING

Town meeting day

THE next Feb'rary, two of the boys — one, a snow painter — stopped with me and decided to stay into March, specially to go to Town Meetin' — never havin' been to one. So, on meetin' day we packed up some noon vittles, hitched up ole Boa's'n and drove out back in good season to git to town hall b'fore the perceedin's got under way.

We found quite a gatherin' of men front the hall b'fore meetin' time, caucussin', and a crowd round little ole "Button" Jones, retired tailer, who wuz airin' his ideas on demicratic gov'ment in his squeaky voice, and "go'dammin'" 'bout how he'd-a organized the country, if he'd-a been in "Abe Washin'ton's" place.

Inside we took seats where the boys could note things good, and found Lute Frisbie had been appinted moderater and wuz callin' the meetin' to order. Then they went through the usual bizness of votin' for town officers, propriatin' money for this, that, and t'other thing, and fixin' the taxes for the next year — all with considable proposin', objectionin', and spattin' back and forth.

Some cur'ous critters do crawl out-a their holes evry year to go to town meetin', which is what in'rests the fellers. They enjoyed seein' ole Sol Hudson from "Slab City" takin' the floor aginst most evrythin' that come up. Sol's a big ox of a man with the glarrin'est eyes and bristlin'est eyebrows you ever see, and looks a tower of stren'th with his mop of ironish red hair (tho actually tim'rous as a rabbit at heart, if you stand up to him).

He alw'ys gits his yearly shearin' on town meetin' day, but not till after the meetin'. For when Will Frisbie has gone over Sol's bumpy scalp with the hoss clippers — leavin' nothin' but bris'les and clipper nicks — Sol puts on a smaller size extry hat he brings with him and shuffles off home, all shorn of his self-importance.

Constable Jubb

THE TOWN CONSTABLE

ALL ten comman'ments probly git busted herebouts as much as other places, but real desprit crimes ain't so common, thanks be!

Freeman Jubb has been an able enough constable, and in his day could wras'le down an ox by the horns (but gorry! Today he's the heftiest man in Jefferson County and too hoofsore to move much).

So fur's I know, he never locked up but one man, and that wuz years ago. A big, weak-headed gawk, called "Bull" Thomas, worked on the town farm at the time, and sudd'nly went ravin'. They say he started an awful hullaballoo in the hen yard, pitchforkin' an ole rooster round, and then took to the woods, rushin' this way and that, a-jabbin' at maginary things with the pitchfork. Of course, the poor folks wuz scared most to death and Freeman wuz sent for to lead the chase, he bein' considable more active them days.

'Twuz easy enough to trail the crazy critter, he wuz yellin' so, but night wuz comin' on and they didn't ketch up with him till dusk, way over by Trap cemetary. Free piled onto Bull's back goin' over the wall, and got his finger bit reachin' for a throat hold.

Hydrifoby, or sumthin'-a the kind set in and Free had to go to Portland and have the finger ampitated.

What little time he has (b'tween meals), week days, Freeman spends in his room at town hall settin' in a special stout chair Milt Kester built for him. Likes to have strangers inquire how he lost his finger, so he kin tell 'em of trailin' "an armed desperaydoe" through the woods on a dark, stormy night, and capturin' him single handed in the back corner of a tomb.

He keeps a fat ole rabbit dog, which he calls a blood houn', but depitises his oldest boy to do anythin' in the way of 'ficial bizness which can't be done settin' down.

Tools of law and order

Getting ready to "fit" wood

CHORES

MAYBE the small jobs a farmer has to do, early and late, wuz called "chores," stead of "work," so it wouldn't seem so much a part of the long day he really puts in. But to a growin' young-un chores is work, and my father see to it that us five boys each done a share soon's we wuz old enough to tote a stick-a wood. A birch switch hung by the kitchen shed door as a reminder, tho seldom used; for we early learnt that when Father looked at us with them gimlet blue eyes of his and told us to do sumthin', he meant it.

As it gen'ly is with boys, 'twuz a choice of evils mongst us in devidin' up the chores; each aimin' to do the ones he didn't like the wust. I favered splittin' wood, bein' handy with an ax. We all hated to saw, so Pa give us a cord foot to do at a time, by turns. Alf perferred the care of hosses, but all of us had to larn to milk a cow and help feed all the stock (and clean up round 'em, which wuz the one job we all fit the most over doin').

Walter, the youngest, would make play of anythin' and didn't much mind chorin' for the hens, pigs or other critters, if nobody interfered with his pranks. And he did think up the erijinalist tomfoolery! One day, I remember, he tied one end of a half yard of shoe thread through a kernel of corn, and t'other end round a bumblebee's body (Lord knows how); then fed the corn to an ole rooster. Wallie wuz dancin' and squealin' at the specticle of the ole bird backin' and sidesteppin' all over the door yard, frantic, with the bee a-buzzin' and circlin' round its head, nigher and nigher, when Pa appeared and collared the little scamp.

But all Wallie ever got in such cases wuz a cuff or two on the pants b'hind and a sermon on bein' kind to "all God's creeters," with Father havin' hard work to keep a straight face.

179

Father

Salvaging

THE WRECK

ACCORDIN' to the ole sayin', "It's an ill wind that blows no-body any good," so you might say that sou'east gale in the fall of ninety-two, which drove the "Alice B." on Alby's Shore, proves the case.

She came wallerin' up the bay that mornin' with a full cargo, the seas pilin' aboard of her arse and her cap'n aimin' to make the Cove. But the tide bein' low, he had to anchor above Crow P'int, poor shelter in a sou'easter. When her chain parted she skinned by Iron Island and struck side of Pudd'n Ledge, bow on. And there a crowd of us see cap'n and crew crawl out on the bowsprit, drop safe in shoal water, and wade ashore through the surf.

Then the ole craft heaved aginst the ledge and soon broke open. And what a time we had salvagin' the stuff that rolled out'f her! She'd been bound for Bangor and way ports with a genral cargo from Bostin, includin': ten ton of winder weights, hardware, drygoods and grocries, lumbrin' supplies, a thousand bushels of oats and corn, and barr'ls of flour, m'lasses, kerosene and rum.

Speakin' of rum: somebody had brung a gallon from the tavern, and half our crowd got drunker'n soap, fallin' over each other or into the water, and fightin' over anythin' they did manage to fish out. But we sober ones took turns propriatin' things as they washed ashore, and get sevral barr'ls-a flour (only wet in a mite), six cheeses, some brooms, cases of raisins, and a heap of other stuff.

One-a Jab's turns a case and a small barr'l come in together, and he nigh had a coniption fit over which to choose 'fore wadin' in, knee-deep, to gaff the biggest, the case (which proved to be card matches, all soaked — and I got the barr'l — strip bacon).

And what Jab had to say wuz most as sulphry as them matches. "Hell!" he howled, and growled it off and on all aft'noon.

"Strippin' her bones"

"Lettie was a-b'ilin'"

THE LIVERY STABLE

SOMEBODY declared once that Will Frisbie must-a been the last one in the back row when the faces wuz handed out. Even his ma (comical ole critter) admits he wuz an awful homely baby and never did outgrow it. "Felt like hidin' the young-un when anybody come in," says she. But Will's looks ain't pervented him accumilatin' quite a little money durin' the years he's run the liv'ry stable and grain shed, and took over and leased out the Sea View House, and one thing and nother. Purty shrewd. Quite a hoss trader too, and keeps a good stable of hoss-flesh (barrin' that ole black skinfull-a bones he still uses to draw the hearse for fun'rals — sometimes — and a ten-doller sway-back he took for a bad debt jest recent, and which ain't fit to earn its hay and oats).

Will rented ole "ten-doller" to Lettie Dicksey last Sund'y, to haul her to camp meetin', her and her sister from Augusty. As you know, the road to the camp ground is all uphill and downdale, and that ole nag moped along, barely one foot ahead of another, all the way, gitt'n 'em to meetin' jest in time for the ben'diction. And when they wuz ready to go home, they found the critter layin' down, sideways, and it took a crew-a men to git him on his feet and under way. At evry hill he'd try to se'down. When, at last, they crep into the liv'ry yard, 'bout dusk, Lettie was a-b'ilin'.

Says she, "Hain't you a nice one, Will Frisbie? Butter wouldn't-a melted in your mouth when you wuz tellin' me what a clever, willin' hoss, this drag-footed, ole w'at-ye-ma-call-him wuz!" — Will lis'nin', as meek as Moses.

"Ye're two-faced, Will Frisbie! that's what you are!"

"Lettie," says he, "if I had two faces, do ye think I'd be a-wearin' this perticler one, specially of a Sund'y?"

183

Will Frisbie

Questioning the "engineer"

"GAS BUGGIES"

WHEN John Dasset come home from his last trip to Portland, 'bout all he could talk about at the store that evenin' wuz of his havin' seen one-a them new gas buggies they been inventin' to the west'ard. He wuz considable excited about it, him alw'ys bein' in'rested in new machinry of all kinds.

He said the thing wuz stopped by a constable as it come into Main Street from the south, the engineer claimin' he'd driv it all the way from Bostin. A big crowd gathered while he give an account of himself, but scattered some when the engine exploded as he wuz windin' her up with a crank. Scared the daylights out'f evry hoss within hearin' too. Oughta be a law aginst 'lowin' such things on a public road, thinks I. But John, he thinks diff-rent; perdictin' they'll be improved jest as steam engines wuz, and some day, moneyed folks will all be havin' 'em.

The rest'f us contended that engines should be for tracks and hosses for roads. Will Frisbie even went so fur as to perdict there might be an uprisin' of the common people, if all the "risticrats" started tearin' round the country in them "stink-waggins" — causin' hoss-runaways, maimin' wimin and childen, and what not.

Then Simple Sam (who'd finished gnawin' off what shreds of meat wuz left on a salt cod skin he'd hauled out the woodbox, washed down with most half a pail-a water) sudd'nly spoke up, all excited; his whiskers a-drippin'. "I do' wan' no dam ole mor-phine buggie 'xplodin' up b'hind me on the road — no sir-ee!"

Which, in a way, expressed the sentiments of most'f us, spite of John's perdiction that gas buggies, gas wagins and gas boats would be as common as hosses and sails inside-a fifty years.

I wonder.

185

A "hoss runaway"

"Whoa!"